Digital Electror
Through
Worked Examp

Other Macmillan titles of related interest

Digital Electronics Through Worked Examples

Norman Bonnett

MACMILLAN

First published 1992 by
THE MACMILLAN PRESS LTD
Houndmills, Basingstoke, Hampshire RG21 2XS
and London
Companies and representatives
throughout the world

ISBN 0–333–53476–X

A catalogue record for this book is available
from the British Library.

Printed in Hong Kong

Reprinted 1993

Contents

INTRO

Preface

There are available many excellent textbooks on both analogue and digital electronics; these range from elementary texts that cover the subject at school level (with a mainly practical approach) to those that are highly advanced and at the fringe of the technologies. It is intended that this book will strike a balance between these two extremes.

This book is intended for first and second year students of electrical and electronic engineering, in particular those studying for Higher National Certificates and Diplomas; it will also be valuable for undergraduates and should complement lecture and other source material. The aim is to enable the student to solve real world problems in a systematic and professional way.

There is a wind of change in engineering education at the moment. It is no longer sufficient to treat engineers and technician engineers simply as the recipients of information, subject them to a heavy diet of lectures, and then demand them to regurgitate these facts in an examination room. In the United Kingdom there is also pressure firstly to move away from conventional laboratory work (where the only decision that generations of students have had to make is whether to have the graph paper vertical or horizontal or what scales to use for the axis;) by moving towards assignment work. Secondly there is pressure to improve the efficiency of the teaching and lecturing process. For too long it has been believed that engineers and technician engineers are an odd body, who unlike other students appear only to be able to receive information when they are lectured to; unlike other students who can obtain and absorb information from source material! Of course this is quite untrue. A student centred approach consistently produces results that are of a higher quality, are easier to transfer to other situations, and more thoroughly learned than those obtained by conventional rote learning.

The approach adopted in this book is that of worked examples, using both the traditional examination question and also assignments that are based both on laboratory work and on literature searches; these latter types of examples use manufacturers' data as the prime source. There is no attempt either to choose, or of choice to ignore, devices at the forefront of technology; a thorough knowledge of the characteristics of key devices is more transferable to new products than a nodding acquaintance with every device in a data book. It is this quality of transferring knowledge from known situations to new and concrete situations that is the hall mark of sound learning.

Acknowledgements

I would like to thank the following manufacturers for being allowed to use information from their data books and catalogues.

Texas Instruments for extracts concerning the following devices: 7400, 7473, 7476, 74LS76A, 7490, 7493A, 7497, 74143, 74LS139A, 74151, 74161A, 74180, 74194 and TBIBPPPAL16LB.

Cypress Semiconductors for extracts on the following device:

CYM1421

Plessey Semiconductors for extracts on the following devices:

ZN426E, ZN435 and ZN437.

RS Components for extracts on the following device: RS74C922 and for the pin-outs for the RS232C line drivers and receivers.

I must acknowledge the help I have received from Malcolm Stewart and his team at Macmillan Education for the very helpful and patient advice and help they have given me.

Thanks also go to the people whose hardware and software I bought and used to produce the book; Amstrad for their PC1640 computer, Digital Research for the GEM drawing package, Timeworks for their DTP system and MicroPro for their Wordstar word processing package. All performed perfectly.

Ben Bennett at The Polytechnic Huddersfield ran the HILO simulations for me, and the students there and at Bradford College provided me with the initial encouragement to pursue the line of teaching and assessment that this book uses; all have my thanks.

Last, and by no means least I must acknowledge the support of my wife Annedore. She tolerated my moods, my irregular hours at the keyboard and shared my joys. *Danke Liebste*.

TO ANNEDORE

1 Basic Digital Theory

INTRODUCTION

This chapter outlines, using worked examples, material that will be required to fully use this book. At the start of each chapter the topics required are listed under the heading Prior Knowledge and if you either think (or later discover as you work through the chapter) that you do not fully understand the material being presented then you should consult the examples referred to before continuing any further.

Q.1.1

(a) Draw the logic diagram symbol and the truth table for each of the following logic gates : AND, NAND, NOT, NOR and OR. Write the Boolean expression for each of the gates with the truth table.

(b) Explain in words what each truth table states about the gate.

A.1.1

AND

The truth table and circuit diagram symbol for a three input AND gate is given in figure 1.1.1.

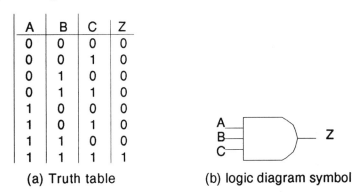

A	B	C	Z
0	0	0	0
0	0	1	0
0	1	0	0
0	1	1	0
1	0	0	0
1	0	1	0
1	1	0	0
1	1	1	1

   (a) Truth table   (b) logic diagram symbol

Figure 1.1.1   Three input AND gate

The Boolean expression for a 3-input AND gate is:
$$Z = A.B.C$$

When ALL the inputs are HIGH the output is HIGH.

1

NAND

The truth table and circuit diagram symbol for a three input NAND gate is given in figure 1.1.2.

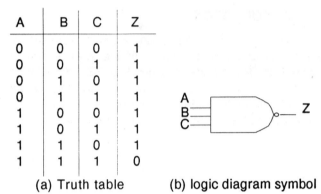

A	B	C	Z
0	0	0	1
0	0	1	1
0	1	0	1
0	1	1	1
1	0	0	1
1	0	1	1
1	1	0	1
1	1	1	0

(a) Truth table   (b) logic diagram symbol

Figure 1.1.2   Three input NAND gate

The Boolean expression for a 3-input NAND gate is:

$$Z = \overline{A.B.C}$$

ANY input that is LOW gives a HIGH output.

NOT

The truth table and circuit diagram symbol for a NOT gate is given in figure 1.1.3.

A	Z
1	0
0	1

(a) truth table   (b) logic diagram symbol

Figure 1.1.3   NOT gate (or inverter)

The Boolean expression for a NOT gate is:

$$Z = \overline{A}$$

When the input is HIGH the output is LOW and vice versa.

NOR

The truth table and circuit diagram symbol for a three input NOR gate is given in figure 1.1.4.

A	B	C	Z
0	0	0	1
0	0	1	0
0	1	0	0
0	1	1	0
1	0	0	0
1	0	1	0
1	1	0	0
1	1	1	0

(a) Truth table   (b) logic diagram symbol

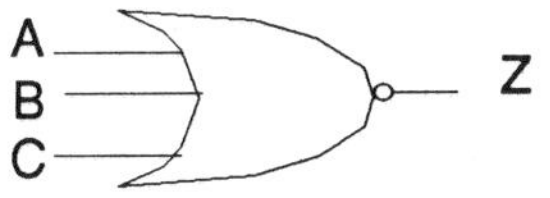

Figure 1.1.4   Three input NOR gate

The Boolean expression for a 3-input NOR gate is

$$Z = \overline{A + B + C}$$

Any HIGH input gives a LOW output.

OR

The truth table and circuit diagram symbol for a two input OR gate is given in figure 1.1.5.

A	B	Z
0	0	0
0	1	1
1	0	1
1	1	1

(a) Truth table   (b) logic diagram symbol

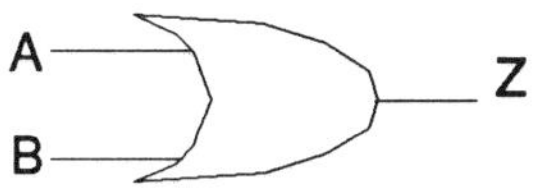

Figure 1.1.5   Two input OR gate

The Boolean expression for a 2-input OR gate is :
$$Z = A + B$$

With any input HIGH the output is HIGH.

Q.1.2 Assignment

Pass a train of clock pulses at a frequency of 2 kHz through a series R-L-C filter consisting of an inductor of 10 mH and a capacitor of 1 microfarad, using resistance values of 100 ohms and 25 ohms (to give values of Q of 1 and 4).

(a) define each of the terms 1-6 below, and

(b) for each of the values of resistance display the resultant waveform across the capacitor on a CRO and measure:

(1) the pulse width,

(2) the pulse amplitude,

(3) the repetition frequency,

(4) the rise time of the pulse before and after the filter,

(5) the overshoot and, where applicable,

(6) the ringing frequency.

A.1.2

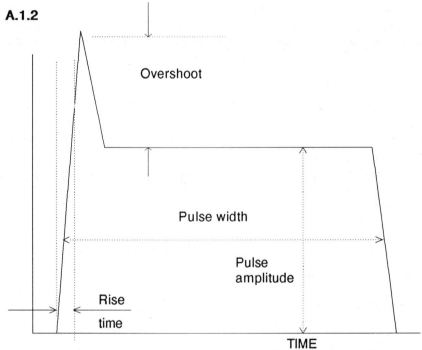

Figure 1.2.1 Time and voltage parameters of a pulse

(a) Definitions

(1) Pulse width

This is the width of the pulse measured at the half-amplitude points of the pulse.(This parameter is sometimes called the half amplitude duration abbreviated to h.a.d.)

(2) Pulse amplitude

This is the amplitude of a pulse measured between its steady state minimum and maximum values.

(3) Repetition frequency

This is the reciprocal of the time for the complete transition of the pulse waveform over one cycle.

(4) Rise time

The rise time of a pulse is measured between 10 and 90% of the mean minimum and maximum values of the pulse's amplitude.

(5) Overshoot

When a pulse is applied to an R-L-C network it is very probable that overshoot will occur. This is a measure of the percentage by which either the maximum or the minimum peaks of the overshoot exceed the mean maximum or the minimum values of amplitude.

(6) Ringing frequency

When a pulse is applied to an R-L-C network it is very possible that any overshoot that is present will also contain some damped oscillatory sine waves. The frequency of these damped sine waves is the ringing frequency.

A computer simulation of the two circuits is shown in figure 1.2.2.

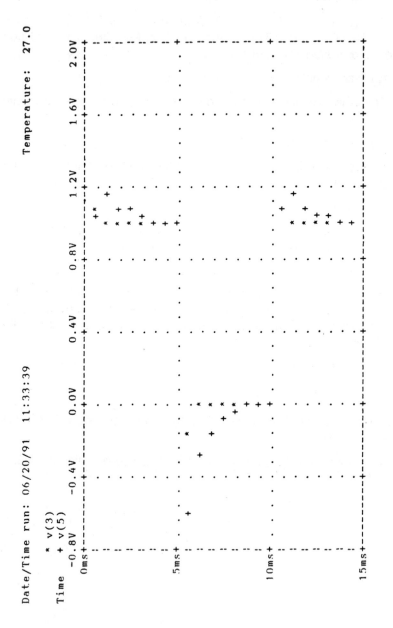

Figure 1.2.2 PSPICE simulation of a filtered pulse

Q.1.3

(a) Draw the logic diagram symbol and the truth table for a 7473 J-K flip-flop, explain what each line of the truth table means and describe an application for a device with that input.

(b) What are master-slave J-K flip-flops, and why are they needed?

(c) Identify from a catalogue, the function of the following J-Ks :

7473, 7476 and 74109.

A.1.3

(a) The truth table and logic diagram symbol for a J-K flip-flop are given in figure 1.3.1.

J	K	Output
0	0	Unchanged
0	1	$Q = 0$
1	0	$Q = 1$
1	1	Toggles

(a) Truth table   (b) logic diagram symbol

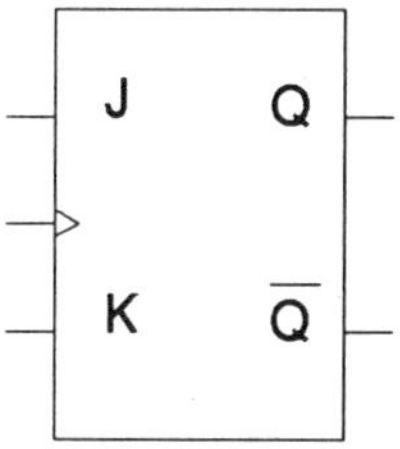

Figure 1.3.1 J-K flip-flop

Figure 1.3.2 is an extract from a manufacturer's handbook for a 7473 TTL IC.

Where an "X" appears in a column it means that this particular input is not important to the result (this is termed a "don't care state").

'73
FUNCTION TABLE

INPUTS				OUTPUTS	
$\overline{CLR}$	CLK	J	K	Q	$\overline{Q}$
L	X	X	X	L	H
H	⊓	L	L	Q_0	$\overline{Q}_0$
H	⊓	H	L	H	L
H	⊓	L	H	L	H
H	⊓	H	H	TOGGLE	

Figure 1.3.2 Function table for a 7473 J–K flip-flop

In the column for CLOCK there is a positive half-cycle of a clock pulse; this is to show that it is during the positive-going half-cycle of the clock pulse that the signals present at the J and K inputs are read into the J-K flip-flop. If the waveform was a negative half-cycle it would indicate that this response to the input signals occurred during the negative half-cycle of the clock pulse waveform. A positive or negative-pointing arrow would indicate that it was the positive or negative-going transition of the clock pulse that initiated the reading of the input signals.

Line 1 means that when the CLR (clear) input is LOW, no matter what the state of the other inputs **the outputs are cleared to the states shown in the function table.** When (as in this case) an input signal is shown with a bar over this indicates that the input is active when the signal there is LOW. When the CLEAR input is HIGH it has no effect on the J-K at all.

Line 2 means that when J = K = 0, then the state of the outputs *does not change* after the clock pulse has occurred. With this input, a data word in the J-K can be retained during a clock pulse cycle.

Line 3 means that **no matter what the state** of the outputs before the clock pulse after the clock pulse the Q output will be a 1. This input would load a 1 into the J-K.

Line 4 means that **no matter what the state** of the outputs before the clock pulse, after the clock pulse the Q output will be a 0. This input would load a 0 into the J-K.

Line 5 means that **every time a clock pulse occurs the outputs of the J-K change over.** This can be illustrated with the state diagram in figure 1.3.3.

This input would cause the output to change 1-0-1, at half the rate at which the clock pulse input was changing 1-0-1.

(b) A master-slave flip-flop contains two J-Ks connected as shown in figure 1.3.4.

The two clock pulse inputs are separated from each other

Figure 1.3.3 State diagram for the toggle mode of a J-K flip-flop

internally by an inverter, so that if they both respond to the positive part of the clock pulse, the master J-K will be able to accept the J and K inputs

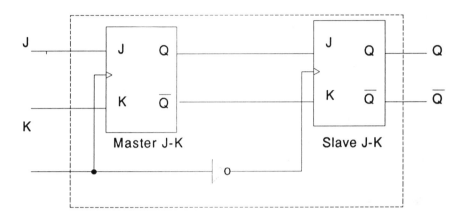

Figure 1.3.4   Basic master-slave J-K flip-flop

as data during the positive half-cycle of the clock; the slave will have this half-cycle inverted and so will have a negative half-cycle applied to it. When the clock is HIGH the slave J-K's outputs are isolated from changes occurring in the master as its clock is LOW. When the clock is LOW the slave is able to accept data from the master as the inverter puts a HIGH on its clock input; while the master cannot accept new data. While the outputs of the slave are changing any new changes at the input of the master cannot be passed to the output of the slave. From observing only the input and output from a master-slave flip-flop and from looking at its logic diagram symbol it is in every way the same as other types of J-K, as the changes occur during one clock pulse cycle. Wherever conditions are changing at the input and it is **not** desired to have these changes immediately present at the output, then a master-slave device will provide this isolation.

(c) Figure 1.3.5. is extracted from a manufacturer's data book entries for TTL J-K flip-flops.

The 7476 is similar to the 7473, but as well as the clear facility there is also a separate preset for each of the J-Ks. This allows either a 1 or a 0 to be set initially in the J-K **without requiring a clock pulse to be present.**

Flip-flops (bistables)

J-K

7473	Dual with clear
7473	Dual with preset and clock
7478	Dual with preset common clear and clock
74109	Dual positive edge triggered preset and clear
74112	Dual negative edge triggered preset and clear

Figure 1.3.5 Extracts from a supplier's catalogue

The 74109 has a positive edge triggered clock input, so that when the clock pulse goes from 0 to 1 it is the rising edge of the clock pulse that causes any changes on the output of the J-K. This means that the J-K accepts as input the states present on the J and K inputs **only during the time of the 0 to 1 transition**. Both J-Ks have all inputs separate.

Q.1.4 Assignment

Quad 2-input NAND gates are used frequently in digital circuits. From manufacturers' data sheets and from catalogues look for and compare the main electrical features of these devices, in both CMOS and TTL technologies.

A.1.4

From the two catalogue extracts in figure 1.4.1 it can be seen that the 7400, 7401 and 7403 are examples of quad (i.e. there are four separate 2-input NAND gates in each IC) 2-input gates in TTL technology; and that the 4001B, the 4011B and the 4011UB are quad 2-input NAND gates in CMOS technology.

The 7400 and 7403 are available from this supplier in a wide range of logic families; and the 7401 in both the Standard and in Low Power Schottky families. Both the 7401 and the 7403 are described as "o.c." (**open collector**) devices. The term open collector refers to circuits that are designed to have an external "pull-up" resistor mounted to the collector of the output transistor. (For further information on open collector devices see Appendix 1.)

TTL Devices

NAND gates

	FAMILIES				
	STD	LS	ALS	HCT	
Quad 2-input	X	X	X	X	7400
Quad 2-input oc	X	X			7401
Quad 2-input oc	X	X	X	X	7403
CMOS Devices					
NAND gates					4011B
Quad 2-input					4011UB
Quad 2-input					4011B

Figure 1.4.1 Extracts from a supplier's catalogue

The 4011B and the 4011UB are also quad 2-input NAND gates. The difference between the two is that the device with a "B" as suffix has its inputs protected against damage due to high static voltages or electrical fields. This does not give unlimited protection to the device and it is always necessary to avoid voltages outside the manufacturer's recommended range. Devices with a suffix "UB" are not buffered and extra care must be taken here to ensure that they are protected against stray static discharges, particularly during soldering and testing operations.

Q.1.5 Assignment

A CNC machine tool has a cooling pump that applies a coolant to prevent the rotating workpiece from overheating; the requirements for coolant depends upon the type of material being cut (variable A in the truth table), the speed of rotation (B), and the amount of material to be removed(C).

The truth table relates these requirements; the logic signal "Z" will start the coolant pump.

(a) Use a Karnaugh map to minimise the truth table.

(b) Draw a circuit diagram for this minimised expression using gates in the 74xxx series.

(c) Apply deMorgan's theorems to produce a function that uses only NAND gates.

A	B	C	Z
0	0	1	1
0	1	0	1
0	1	1	1
1	0	1	1
1	1	1	1

(d) Draw a circuit diagram for this minimised expression using gates in the 74xxx series.

(e) For each of the gates you use, justify the choice made.

A.1.5

(a) The required Karnaugh map is shown below in figure 1.5.1.

To construct this circuit will require :

1 NOT gate type 7404 (Hex inverting buffer)

1 AND gate type 7408 (Quad 2-input)

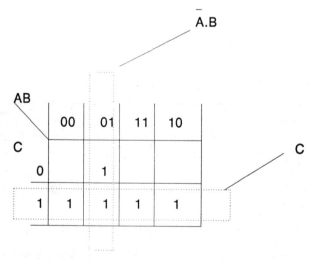

Figure 1.5.1 Karnaugh map for Q.1.5

From this can be read the minimised form of $Z = C + \overline{A}.B$.

1 OR gate type 7432 (Quad 2-input)

There are no special requirements for these gates, they are not clocked at high speeds and no constraints were placed in the question on either power consumption or heat dissipation. Hence it can be assumed that standard TTL ICs can be used; these are normally the cheapest and most readily available range of ICs.

From each of these ICs only one gate will be used but three separate ICs are required. This clearly leaves a total of 11 gates which are not used, and will need a pcb large enough to mount all of the ICs on.

(b) The circuit is shown using these gates in figure 1.5.2.

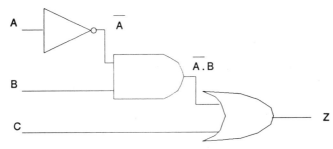

Figure 1.5.2   Minimised circuit

(c) Applying deMorgan's theorems to implement the circuit in NAND gates only gives:

(d) The circuit diagram is given in figure 1.5.3.

This can be implemented with a single 7400 IC, again as there are no constraints on power, heat or speed of operation, the previous criteria still apply, so that a standard TTL device, such as a 7400 is chosen. This gives a chip count of 1, requiring the smallest possible sized piece of pcb; it would be easy to test in the event of faults developing, as all the circuit is built around a single chip, making component identification and signal tracing easier.

This minimisation and the subsequent application of deMorgan's theorems show the power of both techniques and the savings that can be achieved in cost, space, and power consumption by the use of sound design procedures.

$$Z = \overline{\overline{C} + \overline{A}.B}$$

so that

$$Z = \overline{\overline{C}} . \overline{\overline{A}.B}$$

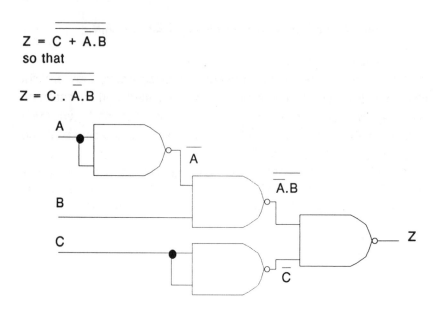

Figure 1.5.3 Minimised form after applying deMorgan's theorems

Q.1.6

(a) Explain why it is necessary to convert signals from analogue to digital, and why it is also necessary to convert from digital to analogue.

(b) There are many different methods of converting analogue signals into digital signals and many ways of converting digital signals into analogue signals. Describe one method of each and compare them on the grounds of speed, cost and fidelity.

A.1.6

(a) Computers and logic circuits work with digital signals, these are always in one of two states: 1 (or "HIGH") or 0 (or "LOW"). An analogue signal can have a very large number of possible amplitude states. In order for a computer to be able to process information from the "analogue world", the information must be converted into digital form. Similarly with the digital form in which data and information are output from computers and logic devices, this must be converted to analogue form before we can understand and use it easily. The digital signals used to send information to the VDU of a computer would be of little use to us, so these must be converted into letters, figures and symbols that we can easily understand.

(b) The methods of converting analogue signals into digital form range from those that are very fast and quite expensive to those that are slow and fairly cheap; the accuracy of the conversion also varies with the method used. They can be broadly put into groups which are OPEN LOOP and those which are CLOSED LOOP. The open loop systems do not have information fed back from the output in order to make decisions at the input whereas the closed loop systems do.

One example of an open loop system is the voltage to frequency converter, and an example of a closed loop system is the staircase and compare converter; these are dealt with below.

Voltage to frequency converters

A diagram of this system is shown in figure 1.6.1.

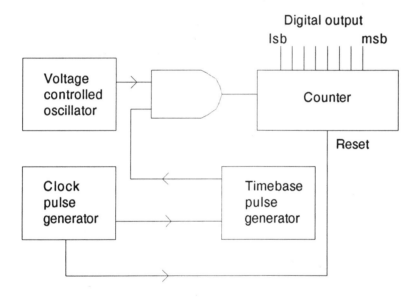

Figure 1.6.1 Voltage-to-frequency ADC

This system applies the analogue input signal to a VCO (a Voltage Controlled Oscillator which is an oscillator whose output frequency is determined by the voltage present at one of its input pins). The output frequency varies linearly with the analogue signal. The oscillator output is fed into a two-input AND gate, the other input of which is a pulse derived from a pulse generator. The counter is firstly reset, and the pulse generator outputs a fixed duration pulse to the AND gate; this, with the output of the VCO, opens the gate and this gated output from the VCO is fed to the counter. At the end of the time period set by the pulse generator, the count is stopped and the binary digits in the counter are proportional to the amplitude of the analogue input signal.

This method is accurate to 0.04% and has a speed which is controlled by the output frequency from the VCO.

Staircase and compare converters

This system generates a staircase waveform from a clock pulse generator and compares its amplitude with that of the input analogue signal. When the two have equal amplitude, the generation stops. As the amplitude of the staircase is derived from the clock pulse generator, the number of pulses that have been generated since the start of conversion is counted, and the count held in the counter represents the binary value of the analogue signal. The staircase waveform is generated in a D-A converter having its input from an external clock pulse generator applied at the "clock" input in figure 1.6.2. The method is cheap, simple and relatively slow; it also requires a dedicated IC. The accuracy is decided by the number of bits used in the conversion. The total system is shown in figure 1.6.2.

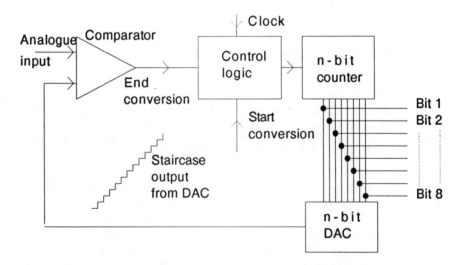

Figure 1.6.2 Staircase and compare ADC, circuit diagram

Q.1.7 Assignment

(a) J-K flip-flops can be used as counters; what feature of the J-Ks truth table is used in a counter?

(b) Describe the main features of synchronous and asynchronous counters. Draw circuit diagrams for, and explain the operation of, each of these counters when they are used for :

(i) a binary counter,

(ii) a BCD counter.

(iii)Explain the main advantages and disadvantages of each type.

A.1.7

(a) The truth table for a J-K flip flop is given in figure 1.7.1.

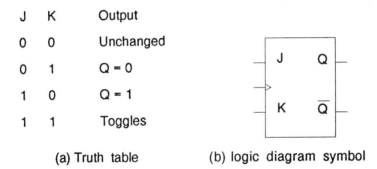

J	K	Output
0	0	Unchanged
0	1	Q = 0
1	0	Q = 1
1	1	Toggles

(a) Truth table   (b) logic diagram symbol

Figure 1.7.1 J-K flip-flop

The last line of the table shows that when J = K = 1, then the output "toggles". This can be explained by a state diagram such as figure 1.7.2; this shows how the output changes on each clock pulse transition, with the Q output changing from 0 - 1 - 0 etc. with each clock pulse.

Figure 1.7.2 State diagram for the toggle mode of a J-K flip-flop

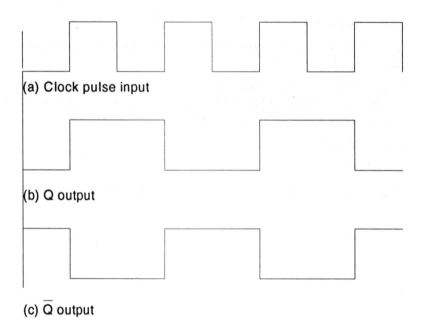

(a) Clock pulse input

(b) Q output

(c) $\overline{Q}$ output

Figure 1.7.3 Divide-by-two waveforms

Figure 1.7.3 shows the input clock pulse train and the outputs.

It can be seen that the outputs change at a rate which is half that of the clock pulse input. In this mode the J-K is operating as a **divide-by-two** device.

(b) (i) - (iii).

In figure 1.7.4. two J-K flip flops are connected together so that all the J and K inputs are connected to HIGH, and clock pulses are applied to the first J-K while the second J-K has its clock pulse input from the Q output of the first J-K.

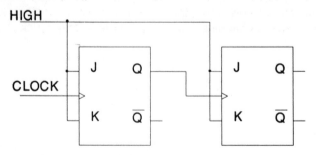

Figure 1.7.4 Divide-by-four asynchronous counter

As both J-Ks will operate in the divide-by-two mode, so the second J-K will have its output at half the frequency of the first J-K's output. As the first J-K's output is at half the clock pulse frequency, then the output from the second J-K is at a quarter of that of the clock pulses. The waveforms are shown in figure 1.7.5. Here the sequence of pulses can be correlated with the changes in the outputs of the two J-Ks; it is only after four clock pulses (1-4) have been applied that the second J-K has completed one complete cycle of changes.

Adding additional J-Ks will give a doubling in modulus for each extra J-K added, so that counters for modulo-8, 16 etc. are easily formed by adding extra J-Ks.

Where more than one J-K is used each additional counter operates from the output of the previous one, and so this type of counter is often referred to as **a ripple through counter.** As each counter must wait until the previous J-K's output has changed before any change can occur, this type of counter is not the fastest available.

To act as BCD (Binary Coded Decimal) counter, a binary counter is used that counts to 16, and the count is stopped after 9 is reached; the counter is then cleared to 0, and the count restarted.

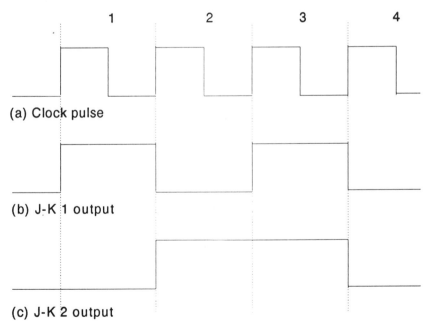

(a) Clock pulse

(b) J-K 1 output

(c) J-K 2 output

Figure 1.7.5 Divide-by-four waveforms

The state diagram for a BCD counter is shown in figure 1.7.6.

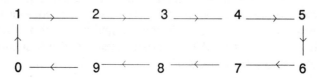

Figure 1.7.6   BCD counter, state diagram

To reset the counter to 0 on the tenth clock pulse requires J-K flip-flops with a CLEAR input. This input is fed from a 2-input NAND gate. The NAND gate has its inputs derived from the outputs of QB and QD, the output of the gate is LOW whenever QB = QD = 1.

This occurs when the counter goes from the 1001 state to the 1010 state on pulse number 10. Once the flip-flops have been cleared the output of the NAND goes HIGH as the state B = D = 1 is no longer present.

As each flip-flop is triggered from the previous one, and as each device will have propagation delays associated with it, there is an overall delay between changes occurring on the first flip-flop and changes on the output of the final one; if the delay for one J-K is 15 ns, then the delay for 5 J-K is clearly 75 ns. These accumulated delays place an upper limit on the frequencies that can be used with asynchronous counters.

When used as a synchronous counter the J-Ks are all triggered at the same time by having the clock pulses applied to all the devices at the same time. Because of this and the fact that synchronous counters operate at higher clock rates than asynchronous counters, it is normal to use **master-slave** flip-flops, so that the output is isolated from changes occurring at the input during a clock pulse cycle.

An example of a mod-16 synchronous counter is shown in figure 1.7.8.

The J and K inputs are not all connected to 1 but have their inputs derived from the result of AND-ing together the outputs of previous J-Ks. The first flip-flop has both its inputs at 1, so that its output will toggle on each clock pulse cycle. The inputs for the next flip-flop are derived from the output of the first one, so that B will only toggle when QA = 1 occurs

at the input **before** a clock pulse occurs; this condition is met when QA
changes from a count of 1 to 2 and from 3 to 4 etc., during the 2-3 period
its output is a 0.

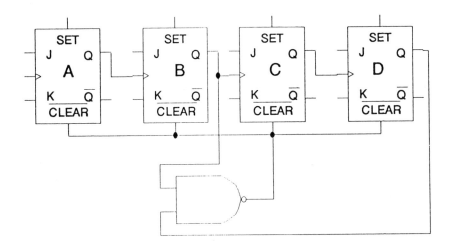

Figure 1.7.7 Circuit diagram for a BCD counter

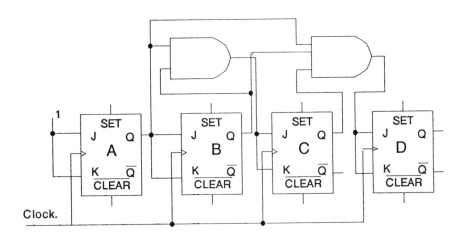

Figure 1.7.8 Mod-16 synchronous counter

Clearly there are changes occurring in the J-Ks which are dependent on the states of other gates. So that the changes at the **input** do not affect the output until these conditions have been set up correctly, some isolation between the input and output would be desirable. This is obtained by using master-slave J-Ks. As the input for QC is derived from AND-ing the outputs from A and B, it can only toggle when QA = QB = 1 is present at the output of the AND gate **before** the clock pulse occurs; this occurs when the count goes from 3 to 4.

Similarly, the input for D is derived from AND-ing the outputs of A, B and C, and so it can only toggle when A = B = C = 1, this occurring when the count goes from 15 to 16.

The truth table for the counter is given in figure 1.7.9.

Count	A	B	C	D
0	0	0	0	0
1	1	0	0	0
2	0	1	0	0
3	1	1	0	0
4	0	0	1	0
5	1	0	1	0
6	0	1	1	0
7	1	1	1	0
8	0	0	0	1
9	1	0	0	1
10	0	1	0	1
11	1	1	0	1
12	0	0	1	1
13	1	0	1	1
14	0	1	1	1
15	1	1	1	1

Figure 1.7.9 Mod-16 synchronous counter, truth table

To produce a synchronous BCD counter requires the counter to be reset to 0 when the count changes from 9 to 10; this needs the outputs of B and D to be NAND-ed together and the output of the NAND gate applied to the CLEAR input of all the master-slave J-K flip-flops. The circuit for this is given in figure 1.7.10.

The delays associated with synchronous counters are the sum of the propagation delays of a single master-slave J-K device plus that of a single AND gate; this is considerably less than for an asynchronous counter.

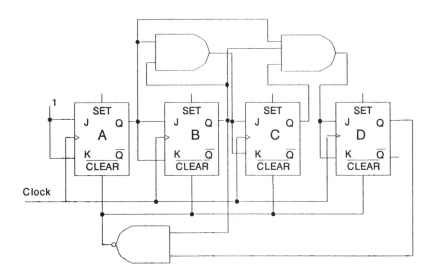

Figure 1.7.10   BCD synchronous counter

2 Manufacturer's Data

2.1 Prior Knowledge

You should be familiar with the following topics:

(a) The truth tables for and the operation of the basic logic gates: AND, NAND, OR, NOR and NOT.

A review question on this topic is contained in **Q.1.1.**

(b) The truth tables for and the main characteristics of J-K flip-flops.

A review question on this topic is contained in **Q.1.2.**

(c) The use of the devices in (b) as both synchronous and asynchronous counters and as shift registers.

A review question on this topic is contained in **Q.1.3.**

2.2 Introduction

This chapter deals with manufacturer's literature; this includes data books and product lists. There are fundamental differences between the information contained in these sources and the use of each is essential in any work involving the use of the devices listed there.

There is no short cut to understanding this material, and time is always well spent in ensuring that the correct source is being used for an item of information, and also that the information is understood. More designs fail because a data sheet was only given a scant reading than fail from either a misunderstanding of a problem or the application of wrong design techniques.

Hints

(a) In looking at some of the timing diagrams and also at truth and function tables it is very useful to have a piece of clear plastic to lay on the line or timing sequence you are examining. It is better than paper because it allows you to see some of the printing under it, so that the sequence of events can be followed more easily.

(b) It would clearly be impractical to give detailed information on every device discussed in this book. Many technical libraries have these data books available and it is a sound idea to locate such a library and consult these data books to extend your knowledge of the devices as you work through the text.

(c) The order in which the devices are presented has been chosen to lead you through the data books in a way which increases the complexity of the devices and also introduces other ideas about data sheets. Hence while such factors as HIGH and LOW logic input and output levels are given detailed treatment in the simpler devices, the emphasis moves towards other features in more complex devices, with perhaps no mention of the former unless it is of special interest for that device.

Q.2.1 Library assignment

(a) The following are all types of logic families. Explain the significant features of each family, and arrange the development of the families in chronological order.

RTL, DTL, 74xx, 4xxx, 74LSxx, 74ALSxx, 74ACxx, 74HCxx, 74ACTxx, 74HCTxx, 74BCTxx, 4xxxB.

(b) Sketch a graph of average gate propagation delay against power consumption for the 4xxx, HC, ALS, LS, TTL, ACL and FAST ranges.

A.2.1

RTL (resistor-transistor logic) was introduced in the early 1960s. As the name suggests the logic circuits were made from resistors and transistors; they were the first truly integrated circuit logic devices. The transistors had slow switching times. There was also the need to operate at a low value of V_{CC}, so that the difference between a HIGH output and a LOW was often not sufficient to give reliable circuit action.

DTL (diode-transistor logic) was introduced by Signetics in the mid-1960s. The inputs to all the gates were via diodes which acted as switches; the circuits dissipated about 12-18 mW per gate. Their chief drawback was the way in which the output circuit was configured. With this configuration there was a large output impedance present; this makes the family very prone to noise and hence to faulty circuit operation.

74xx is the series known as TTL (transistor-transistor logic) and was developed in the early 1970s; the name reflects the fact that all the logic elements are constructed from transistors. The numbering system for the series, 74xx, is still used today for devices in this range.

Under certain switching conditions they source a large current to the 0 V rail. When several devices do this, a very large surge of current is required from the power supply. This can cause problems when a poorly regulated or high impedance supply is used.

4xxx is the numbering sequence used for CMOS (complementary metal-oxide semiconductor) devices. These were developed during the early 1970s, in order to remedy some of the perceived problems with the TTL family. These work from a supply voltage from +3 to +12 V rather than the 5 V required for the 74xx series and have a zero quiescent current demand. They are slower than the TTL family, having lower clock pulse rates and are very easily damaged by static charges. These often occur during the installation of the devices so that no matter how good the design, the resultant circuits often fail to work "first time".

74LSxx; this low power Schottky family has a Schottky diode fitted between the base and collector of the output devices so that the transistors are not driven into saturation; this causes the speed of operation to improve by a factor of about 3-4 over the normal 74xx devices. They dissipate about a quarter of the power of normal TTL ICs.

FAST devices have even faster clocking rates than the 74LSxx series; this range has numbering in the 74Fxx series. They dissipate about the same amount of power as do the 74LSxx series.

The 74ALSxx series gives twice the operating speed for half the power consumption of LS devices.

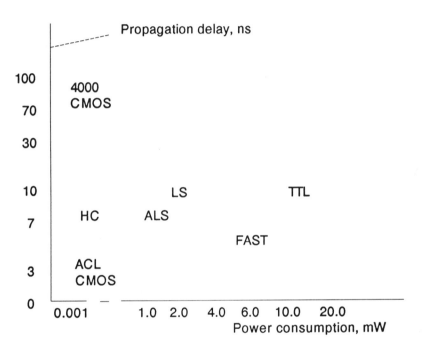

Figure 2.1.1   Propagation against power consumption for families
of gates

4xxxB are CMOS devices which have buffers fitted to the inputs for better protection from static discharges. Many of the original 4xxx family of devices were neither reliable nor predictable. This range has none of those shortcomings.

74HCT and 74ACT are respectively the High speed CMOS and the Advanced CMOS ranges. Here the operation of the devices is as fast as the TTL range but with the advantage of drawing no standing current.

The numbering series for both the ranges is the same as for the TTL 74xx range of devices. The 74HCT and 74ACT ranges require a higher input voltage than the current NMOS devices found in much microprocessor circuitry can supply. The 74ACTxx range has TTL input voltage level compatibility.

The 74HCT series of devices are high speed CMOS, with their inputs configured as direct drop-in replacement for LS TTL devices.

(b) The required diagram is shown in figure 2.1.1.

Q.2.2

(a) From the data sheets for a 7400, find the values of the following parameters and explain what the implication is of each parameter:

(1) function,

(2) supply voltage,

(3) logic levels,

(4) noise immunity,

(5) power dissipation,

(6) fan in/out,

(7) speed-propagation delay,

(8) timing,

(9) size and

(10) packaging.

(b) Explain what is meant by "worst-case-worst-case " philosophy applied to digital IC devices. What is the implication of this philosophy for 74 series devices?

A.2.2

(a) The 7400 is described as a **"quadruple 2-input positive NAND gate"** in figure 2.2.1, which is an extract from a manufacturer's data book; each IC will thus contain four NAND gates each with two inputs working with positive logic levels, i.e. a HIGH or "1" is in the positive (+) direction.

The circuit diagram symbol and the view of the IC's pins (often referred to as the "pin-out") in figure 2.2.1 shows that pins 1 and 2 are

- Package Options Include Both Plastic and Ceramic Chip Carriers in Addition to Plastic and Ceramic DIPs
- Dependable Texas Instruments Quality and Reliability

description

These devices contain four independent 2-input NAND gates.

The SN5400, and SN54LS00, and SN54S00 are characterized for operation over the full military temperature range of −55°C to 125°C. The SN7400, SN74LS00, and SN74S00 are characterized for operation from 0°C to 70°C.

FUNCTION TABLE (each gate)

INPUTS		OUTPUT
A	B	Y
H	H	L
L	X	H
X	L	H

logic diagram (each gate)

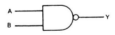

positive logic

$$Y = \overline{A \cdot B} \text{ or } Y = \overline{A} + \overline{B}$$

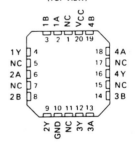

Figure 2.2.1 7400 general information

the inputs of NAND gate 1 and pin 3 is the output of that gate; and pins 12 and 13 are the inputs to gate number 4 and pin 11 is its output, pin 7 is the 0 V connection and pin 14 is the V_{CC} connection. (While logic diagrams tend to ignore the fact that ICs require these latter two connections, attempts are often made to construct circuits exactly as in the logic diagram; ICs need power applied to them.) The IC is available in different packages depending on the technology that is used in manufacture and so three sets of pin-outs are given. The upper of the three is by far the most widely used and is normally called the 14-pin DIL package (14-pin dual in line). Manufacturers use terms such as "J package" to identify the construction as a ceramic-based encapsulation of the "active" part of the IC. It is also available in an N package; this has a plastic compound for encapsulation. (Details of both J and N packages are shown in Appendix 2, (a) and (b) respectively.) Unless otherwise stated in a catalogue, it is normal to expect that the packaging will be type N; (this is usually shown by using 7400N to mean a 7400 in an N package).

Figure 2.2.2 shows another extract from a manufacturer's data sheet.

Line 1 V_{CC}

The voltage supply required for an IC is a very important parameter. It is normally quoted as V_{CC}, and as well as the recommended voltage level, there are also the maximum and minimum voltages that can be applied for "worst-case-worst-case" performance.

Lines 2 and 3 logic levels

		SN5400			SN7400			UNIT
		MIN	NOM	MAX	MIN	NOM	MAX	
V_{CC}	Supply voltage	4.5	5	5.5	4.75	5	5.25	V
V_{IH}	High-level input voltage	2			2			V
V_{IL}	Low-level input voltage			0.8			0.8	V
I_{OH}	High-level output current			-0.4			-0.4	mA
I_{OL}	Low-level output current			16			16	mA
T_A	Operating free-air temperature	-55		125	0		70	°C

Figure 2.2.2 7400 recommended operating instructions

These define the currents and voltages that are either present or required to effect reliable operation.

V_{IH} is the voltage that is needed to give a logical 1 or HIGH at the input of a gate. If the voltage is **below** this level it will not be treated as HIGH. So for the 7400, all input voltages greater than 2 V are treated as HIGH input voltages.

V_{IL} is the voltage that is needed to give a logical 0 or LOW at the input of a gate. If the voltage is **above** this level it will not be treated as LOW. So any input voltage below 0.8 V is treated as a LOW input voltage.

Lines 4 and 5, current at logic inputs and outputs

I_{OH} is the current that flows **from** an output when a logic 1 is present at the output. The load conditions presented to the output are also specified.

I_{OL} is the current that flows **from** an output when a logic 0 is present at the output. The load conditions presented to the output are also specified.

Line6, operating temperature

T_A is the range of temperatures within which the device will operate.

The electrical characteristics are shown in figure 2.2.3.

PARAMETER	TEST CONDITIONS †	SN5400			SN7400			UNIT
		MIN	TYP‡	MAX	MIN	TYP‡	MAX	
V_{IK}	V_{CC} = MIN, I_I = − 12 mA			− 1.5			− 1.5	V
V_{OH}	V_{CC} = MIN, V_{IL} = 0.8 V, I_{OH} = − 0.4 mA	2.4	3.4		2.4	3.4		V
V_{OL}	V_{CC} = MIN, V_{IH} = 2 V, I_{OL} = 16 mA		0.2	0.4		0.2	0.4	V
I_I	V_{CC} = MAX, V_I = 5.5 V			1			1	mA
I_{IH}	V_{CC} = MAX, V_I = 2.4 V			40			40	μA
I_{IL}	V_{CC} = MAX, V_I = 0.4 V			− 1.6			− 1.6	mA
I_{OS}§	V_{CC} = MAX	− 20		− 55	− 18		− 55	mA
I_{CCH}	V_{CC} = MAX, V_I = 0 V		4	8		4	8	mA
I_{CCL}	V_{CC} = MAX, V_I = 4.5 V		12	22		12	22	mA

† For conditions shown as MIN or MAX, use the appropriate value specified under recommended operating conditions.
‡ All typical values are at V_{CC} = 5 V, T_A = 25°C.
§ Not more than one output should be shorted at a time.

Figure 2.2.3 7400 electrical characteristics over recommended free-air temperatures range

V_{OH} is the voltage that is present at the output of a gate, when the output is at logic 1 or HIGH. The minimum value that V_{OH} can have is also normally specified.

V_{OL} is the voltage that is present at the output of a gate, when the output is at logic 0 or LOW. The maximum value of V_{OL} is also normally specified.

I_I is the current that flows into the device when the input voltage is at 5.5 V.

I_{IH} is the current that flows **into** an input when a logic 1 is applied to the input.

I_{IL} is the current that flows **into** an input when a logic 0 is applied to the input.

I_{OS} is the current that flows into an output when one (and **only** one) of the outputs is short-circuited to a ground potential.

I_{OH} is specified at a maximum value of 0.4 mA and I_{IH} as 0.04 mA, so that the maximum number of 7400 gates that could be driven from one output is 0.4 mA/0.04 mA = 10. This latter value is referred to as the **fan out** of the gate, and is important as it shows how many gates can be connected to a single gate and still retain reliable operation. If it is necessary to drive more than 10 gates then a buffer or buffers can be connected to the output used to give a larger fan out.

Power dissipation

The amount of power that an IC needs is an important parameter. It is one of the reasons for the development of low power TTL devices (such as the 74ALS-, 74LS- and 74AC-, ACT- and HCT ranges) as well as the MOS families.

This parameter can be presented in various ways:

P_D is the average power dissipation.

I_{CC} is the current that is taken from the IC's power supply, the power then being calculated using the value of V_{CC} present in the circuit. I_{CC} can vary depending on whether all the outputs of the device are HIGH or whether they are LOW. Two values may be given: I_{CCH} will be used when all the outputs are HIGH, and I_{CCL} when all the outputs are LOW.

Noise immunity

Noise can be defined as "any unwanted signal that is present in a circuit". Usually these unwanted signals will have been induced by magnetic or electrical fields other than those which should normally be present. These signals can cause a well designed and implemented circuit to malfunction. With digital circuits this normally happens when the noise makes the voltage at one or more of the inputs to a gate or circuit either **increase** so that a LOW is taken by the circuit to be a HIGH; or **decrease** so that a HIGH is taken to be a LOW. These are extreme cases and normally the noise only moves the voltage level at the input into the area where unreliable operation can occur. It is the ability of a circuit to tolerate these noise voltages that is referred to as its **noise immunity**.

Any voltage above V_{OH} present at the output is taken to be a HIGH and any voltage below V_{OL} is taken to be a LOW. These are the normal output signals, and no voltages in between these two levels should be present at the output. The input requirements for HIGH and LOW are that a voltage level above $V_{IH(min)}$ which is present at an input is taken to be a HIGH, and any voltage level lower than V_{IL} is treated as a LOW. Inputs lying between these two levels again should not normally be present.

These voltage levels are shown in figure 2.2.4.

The difference between the lowest allowable value of V_{OH} (the HIGH voltage output level, and the lowest permitted value of V_{IH} (the HIGH voltage input level), for reliable circuit operation is called **the high-state noise margin** and can be defined as:

$$V_{NH} = V_{OH(min)} - V_{IH(min)}$$

Should a noise spike or a transient occur that exceeds (even momentarily) the high-state noise margin, then the voltage would drop into the indeterminate range and faulty or unpredictable operation could occur.

There is also a **low-state noise margin** that can be defined as:

$$V_{NL} = V_{IL(max)} - V_{OL(max)}$$

Should a noise spike or a transient occur that causes the voltage to rise by more than this margin then the voltage would rise into the

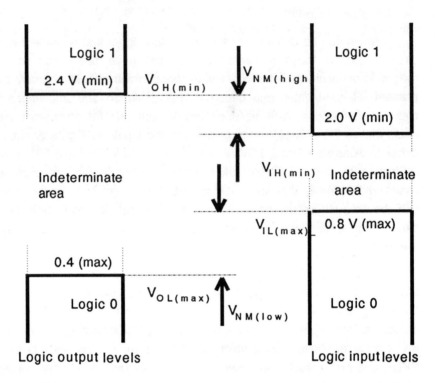

Figure 2.2.4 TTL high and low noise margins

indeterminate range and faulty or unpredictable operation could occur. With the minimum value of V_{CC} and the maximum operating temperature and assuming that the fan-out of 10 is not exceeded then the output HIGH voltage will never be below 2.4 V. This is important because the input HIGH voltages are guaranteed for a **minimum** voltage of 2.0 V; anything in excess of that (e.g. the 2.4 V high output) is treated as a logic 1, and the device will operate satisfactorily.

(b) "Worst-case-worst-case" is a term used by manufacturers to explain their design parameters, and hence the user's limits in which the device will operate. Each of these worst-case parameters is usually given at the lowest or highest value of that parameter which gives satisfactory output, so that the minimum value of V_{CC} together with the minimum allowable value of V_{IH} would still be treated by the device as an allowable set of conditions and the truth or function table for that device would still apply. Similarly, if the maximum and/or minimum values of any of the other parameters are reached but **not** exceeded, then the device will operate normally.

Figure 2.2.5 gives one of the tables for the three sets of data for the electrical performance of the IC. The table refers to the conditions of loading given, the time taken for a transition from a LOW to a HIGH state is shown as being between 11 and 22 ns and for a transition from HIGH to LOW of between 7 ns and 15 ns; both these time ranges refer to the time it takes for a change of logic level at the input to cause a change of logic level at the output. The other two tables (not reproduced here) show that as the values of RL are altered, so are the propagation times and the other electrical characteristics.

Q.2.3 Assignment

Using a catalogue and a manufacturer's data sheet, explain what a 7476 device is and what the entries on the data sheet mean.

How does the 74LS76 differ from the 7476 ?

A.2.3

PARAMETER	FROM (INPUT)	TO (OUTPUT)	TEST CONDITIONS		MIN	TYP	MAX	UNIT
t_{PLH}	A or B	Y	$R_L = 400\,\Omega,$	$C_L = 15\,pF$			11 22	ns
t_{PHL}							7 15	ns

Figure 2.2.5 7400 switching characteristics

The entry in the catalogue shown in figure 2.3.1 describes the 7476 as a "dual J-K flip-flop with preset and clear". It is a standard TTL device. In each IC there will then be two such devices, each independent of the other except for sharing common V_{CC} and 0 V supplies.

The data sheet of figure 2.3.2 gives a pin-out for the devices and also a function table; a general description of the devices is also included.

The function table starts with two columns "Inputs", and "Outputs". Under the "Inputs" column are columns dealing with:

(1) the preset input,

(2) the clear input,

(3) the clock input, and

(4) the J and K inputs.

Both PRE and CLR have bars over them, this means that they are ACTIVE LOW; when a 0 is applied to the inputs they are enabled.

Flip-flops (bistables)

J-K

7473   Dual with clear

7476   Dual with preset clear

7478   Dual with preset common clear and clock

74109   Dual positive edge triggered preset and clear

Figure 2.3.1 Catalogue entry for J-K flip-flops

Line 1 of the function table tells us that if the PRESET input is LOW (L) and the CLEAR input is HIGH (H), then no matter what the signals present on the CLOCK or the J and K inputs (X = **don't care)** the Q output will be HIGH. These are the conditions to PRESET the flip-flop.

Line 2 of the table shows that when PRESET is HIGH and CLEAR is LOW, then the state of the CLOCK and the J and K inputs do not matter as the Q output will be LOW. These are the conditions to CLEAR the flip-flop.

Line 3 of the table shows that when both PRESET and CLEAR are LOW at the same time, then both the outputs from the flip-flop are HIGH. This state is unstable and as the two outputs are logically opposite to

SN5476, SN54LS76A...J OR W PACKAGE
SN7476 ... J OR N PACKAGE
SN74LS76A ... D, J OR N PACKAGE
(TOP VIEW)

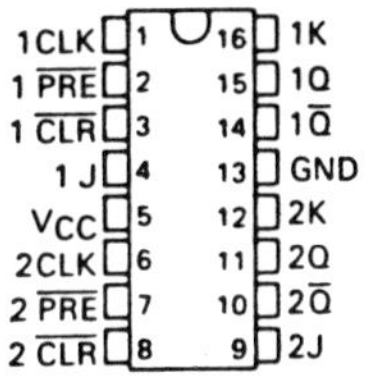

```
 1CLK [ 1      16 ] 1K
 1 PRE [ 2      15 ] 1Q
 1 CLR [ 3      14 ] 1Q̄
   1 J [ 4      13 ] GND
  Vcc [ 5      12 ] 2K
 2CLK [ 6      11 ] 2Q
 2 PRE [ 7      10 ] 2Q̄
 2 CLR [ 8       9 ] 2J
```

'76
FUNCTION TABLE

INPUTS					OUTPUTS	
PRE	CLR	CLK	J	K	Q	Q̄
L	H	X	X	X	H	L
H	L	X	X	X	L	H
L	L	X	X	X	H†	H†
H	H	⊓	L	L	Q₀	Q̄₀
H	H	⊓	H	L	H	L
H	H	⊓	L	H	L	H
H	H	⊓	H	H	TOGGLE	

'LS76A
FUNCTION TABLE

INPUTS					OUTPUTS	
PRE	CLR	CLK	J	K	Q	Q̄
L	H	X	X	X	H	L
H	L	X	X	X	L	H
L	L	X	X	X	H†	H†
H	H	↓	L	L	Q₀	Q̄₀
H	H	↓	H	L	H	L
H	H	↓	L	H	L	H
H	H	↓	H	H	TOGGLE	
H	H	H	X	X	Q₀	Q̄₀

† This configuration is nonstable; that is, it will not persist
when either preset or clear returns to its inactive (high)
level.

Figure 2.3.2 SN7476 and SN74LS76A general information

each other (when one is HIGH the other is LOW), this state should not
exist; as soon as either of the two inputs is taken either HIGH or LOW the
state is removed.

Line 4 of the table shows that when PRESET and CLEAR are both
HIGH and a "1" is applied to the CLOCK, then with the J and K inputs
LOW there is no change at the output; the states present when the clock
pulse occurs are those present after the pulse.

**For the remaining lines of the function table PRESET and
CLEAR are assumed to be high.**

Line 6 of the table shows that when the CLOCK is HIGH then if J = 1 and K = 0, the output Q is at 1.

Line 7 of the table shows that when the CLOCK is HIGH, J = 0 and K = 1, Q = 0 and Q =1.

Line 8 of the table shows that when the CLOCK is HIGH and J and K are both HIGH then the device **toggles** , i.e. the logic levels on the outputs change over.

As well as dealing with the 7476 the data sheet also shows how the 74LS76 functions. This is a low power Schottky device which has a performance slightly different from the 7476 TTL IC.

Lines 4-8 show in the column for CLOCK a downward pointing arrow instead of the positive pulse shown for the 7476. This indicates that the LS device's clock is triggered by the **negative-going edge** of the clock pulse and not by the clock being HIGH; devices such as the 74LS76 are called **negative edge triggered** devices. The 74109 is an example of a **positive edge triggered device.**

			SN54LS76A			SN74LS76A			UNIT
			MIN	NOM	MAX	MIN	NOM	MAX	
V_{CC}	Supply voltage		4.5	5	5.5	4.75	5	5.75	V
V_{IH}	High-level input voltage		2			2			V
V_{IL}	Low-level input voltage				0.7			0.8	V
I_{OH}	High-level output current				− 0.4			− 0.4	mA
I_{OL}	Low-level output current				4			8	mA
f_{clock}	Clock frequency		0		30	0		30	MHz
t_w	Pulse duration	CLK high	20			20			ns
		PRE or CLR low	25			25			
t_{su}	Setup time before CLK↓	data high or low	20			20			ns
		CLR inactive	20			20			
		PRE inactive	25			25			
t_h	Hold time-data after CLK↓		0			0			ns
T_A	Operating free-air temperature		− 55		125	0		70	°C

Figure 2.3.3 74LS76A, operating conditions

Figure 2.3.3 shows the operating conditions for the 74LS76A, the minimum duration for the CLOCK, PRESET AND CLEAR pulses are given, as is their maximum value of the clock pulse frequency. Changes occurring at the input of a J-K are in the form of data words with finite rise and fall times, similarly the clock-pulse input will also have finite rise and fall times. It is possible that additional distortion could also increase these times. When a change occurs at the input it is therefore possible that these rise and fall times in a **level triggered** J-K are such as to cause malfunction of the circuit, due to the fact that the clock pulse is finished before the data word has been input to the J-K. With edge triggered devices the chance of malfunction is reduced as the edge itself is used to clock the J-K and not the HIGH level of the clock pulse.

Also quoted are times for the SET UP TIME, this is the minimum time that input data must be available before a clock-pulse is applied. These lines mean that the data signals at the J and K inputs, together with the CLEAR and PRESET inputs must be present for this time period before a clock pulse is applied. No value is quoted in this instance for the HOLD TIME for the data inputs; a value quoted here would mean that data needs to be present for the specified amount of time **after** a clock-pulse has been applied.

The table of switching characteristics in figure 2.3.4 gives information on how quickly the device operates and under what conditions the test was carried out.

switching characteristics, V_{CC} = 5 V, T_A = 25°C (see note 3)

PARAMETER	FROM (INPUT)	TO (OUTPUT)	TEST CONDITIONS	MIN	TYP	MAX	UNIT
f_{max}				15	20		MHz
t_{PLH}	$\overline{PRE}$ or $\overline{CLR}$	Q or $\overline{Q}$	R_L = 400 Ω, C_L = 15 pF		16	25	ns
t_{PHL}					25	40	ns
t_{PLH}	CLK	Q or $\overline{Q}$			16	25	ns
t_{PHL}					25	40	ns

Figure 2.3.4 SN7476 switching characteristics

Line 1 of the table in figure 2.3.4 gives the minimum and the typical values for the clock frequency; for a 7476 device these are 15 and 20 MHz respectively.

Lines 2 and 3 give the time in ns it takes for a change in the output from LOW to HIGH and also from HIGH to LOW when the preset condition is active. This time is measured after the PRESET line is asserted. Differing times are quoted for the delays respectively 16 ns and 25 ns.

Lines 4 and 5 give similar times for LOW to HIGH and HIGH to LOW transitions when the clear line is asserted.

Lines 6 and 7 give the delay times delay that occur when the clock pulse goes HIGH. Again the times differ depending on whether the transition is from LOW to HIGH or from HIGH to LOW.

The table in figure 2.3.4 also gives guidance about the maximum rate at which switching can occur and about the times before changes at the input occur as changes at the output.

Q.2.4 Assignment

Show how a 74194 device could be used :

(a) as a modem receiver,

(b) as a modem transmitter.

A.2.4

The 74194 is described in figure 2.4.1 as a 4-bit universal shift register. This means that it can be used for:

serial-in/serial out,

parallel-in/serial-out,

serial-in/parallel-out, and

parallel-in/parallel-out data transfer.

It can also be used to shift data words in either a right or a left-hand direction in the register.

The device itself is a 16-pin DIL chip that has pin 8 for 0 V and pin 16 for $+V_{CC}$ of 5 V.

Pin 1 is the CLEAR and from the bar over CLR it is seen that the CLEAR input is ACTIVE LOW; this means that when the clear input is 0 the register is cleared to 0 on all inputs. Normally the CLEAR input will be held HIGH when data is being received, transmitted or stored.

Pin 2 is the SHIFT RIGHT SERIAL INPUT; serial data is input

here, when data is to be shifted in the direction QA towards QD.

Pins 3-6 inclusive are the parallel inputs enabling direct setting of the output to these inputs.

Pin 7 is the SHIFT LEFT SERIAL INPUT; serial data is input here when the data is to be shifted in the direction QD towards QA.

Pins 9 and 10 set the MODE of the device; whether these are HIGH or LOW decides in which of the four possible modes the register functions:

(1) Inhibit the clock (often called **do nothing**).

(2) Shift data right in the direction QA towards QD.

(3) Shift data left in the direction QD towards QA.

(4) Parallel load data directly from the A-D input pins.

- **Parallel Inputs and Outputs**
- **Four Operating Modes:**
  Synchronous Parallel Load
  Right Shift
  Left Shift
  Do Nothing
- **Positive Edge-Triggered Clocking**
- **Direct Overriding Clear**

SN54194, SN54LS194A, SN54S194 . . . J OR W PACKAGE
SN74194 . . . J OR N PACKAGE
SN74LS194A, SN74S194 . . . D, J OR N PACKAGE
(TOP VIEW)

$\overline{CLR}$ [1	16]	V_{CC}
SR SER [2	15]	Q_A
A [3	14]	Q_B
B [4	13]	Q_C
C [5	12]	Q_D
D [6	11]	CLK
SL SER [7	10]	S1
GND [8	9]	S0

TYPE	TYPICAL MAXIMUM CLOCK FREQUENCY	TYPICAL POWER DISSIPATION
'194	36 MHz	195 mW
'LS194A	36 MHz	75 mW
'S194	105 MHz	425 mW

Figure 2.4.1 SN74194 general information

Pin 11 is the CLOCK PULSE input; it is common for all the gates in the IC.

Pins 12-15 inclusive are the parallel outputs from the register. QD also functions as the SHIFT RIGHT SERIAL DATA OUT pin when this output mode is selected.

Line 1 in the function table in figure 2.4.2 shows that when CLEAR is LOW (and irrespective of any other input) all the outputs are CLEARED to LOW.

Line 2 shows that when CLEAR is HIGH (as it normally is, except when clearing the registers) and the clock is LOW, then the outputs on pins 12-15 remain unchanged no matter what changes occur at the other inputs; this is the INHIBIT or **do nothing** mode.

FUNCTION TABLE

CLEAR	MODE		CLOCK	SERIAL		PARALLEL				OUTPUTS			
	S1	S0		LEFT	RIGHT	A	B	C	D	Q_A	Q_B	Q_C	Q_D
L	X	X	X	X	X	X	X	X	X	L	L	L	L
H	X	X	L	X	X	X	X	X	X	Q_{A0}	Q_{B0}	Q_{C0}	Q_{D0}
H	H	H	↑	X	X	a	b	c	d	a	b	c	d
H	L	H	↑	X	H	X	X	X	X	H	Q_{An}	Q_{Bn}	Q_{Cn}
H	L	H	↑	X	L	X	X	X	X	L	Q_{An}	Q_{Bn}	Q_{Cn}
H	H	L	↑	H	X	X	X	X	X	Q_{Bn}	Q_{Cn}	Q_{Dn}	H
H	H	L	↑	L	X	X	X	X	X	Q_{Bn}	Q_{Cn}	Q_{Dn}	L
H	L	L	X	X	X	X	X	X	X	Q_{A0}	Q_{B0}	Q_{C0}	Q_{D0}

H = high level (steady state)
L = low level (steady state)
X = irrelevant (any input, including tran-sitions)
↑ = transition from low to high level
a, b, c, d = the level of steady state input at inputs A, B, C, or D, respectively.
Q_{A0}, Q_{B0}, Q_{C0}, Q_{D0} = the level of Q_A, Q_B, Q_C, or Q_D, respectively, before the indicated steady state input conditions were established.
Q_{An}, Q_{Bn}, Q_{Cn}, Q_{Dn} = the level of Q_A, Q_B, Q_C, respectively, before the most-recent ↑ transition of the clock.

Figure 2.4.2 SN74194 function table

Line 3 shows CLEAR as HIGH and both of the MODE inputs also HIGH. This is the mode in which PARALLEL LOADING of the registers occurs. This is shown by the columns under the heading "outputs", where these have the same value as the parallel inputs A, B, C and D.

Line 4 has MODE INPUT 1 at LOW and MODE INPUT 2 at HIGH. This is the normal **shift right** mode of the shift register. When pin 2 (the serial data input) is HIGH, then QA is made HIGH and the other bits are shifted one bit to the right on a positive edge of the clock pulse, so that QB takes the value assigned before the clock pulse to QA; all the other bits are also shifted to the right, (this will be explained again when the waveforms are examined).

Line 5 has MODE INPUT 1 at LOW and MODE INPUT 2 HIGH, this is still the **shift right** mode of the shift register. However pin 2 (the serial data input) is now LOW so that QA is made LOW and the other bits are shifted one bit to the right on a **positive** edge of the clock pulse, so that QB takes the value assigned **before** the clock pulse to QA; all the other bits are also shifted to the right.

Line 6 has MODE INPUT 1 at HIGH and MODE INPUT 2 at LOW. This is the **shift left** mode of the register; when pin 7 is HIGH and a positive edge of a clock pulse occurs this HIGH is stored in QD, the other bits are shifted to the left.

Line 7 has MODE INPUT 1 at HIGH and MODE INPUT 2 at LOW, this is the SHIFT LEFT mode of the register; when pin 7 is LOW and a positive edge of a clock pulse occurs this LOW is stored in QD, and the other bits are shifted to the left.

Line 8 shows both pins 9 and 10 LOW; this is again a DO NOTHING mode.

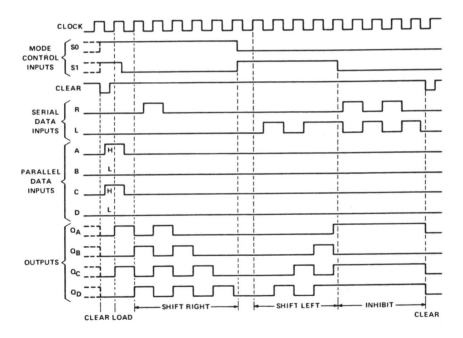

Figure 2.4.3 SN74194 typical pulse sequence

Figure 2.4.3 shows a typical set of sequences. The top waveform is the clock pulse train with the other inputs shown on the left-hand side of the waveform diagram; the bottom line shows how the various modes in which the register is working can occur.

During the time allocated to CLEAR, the clear input is taken LOW and all the outputs QA-QD are taken LOW. The CLEAR is then taken HIGH. It should be noted that at the time CLEAR goes HIGH both S0 and S1 are also HIGH, so that the register is prepared for **parallel load.**

At the next positive-going edge of the clock pulse the data present on the PARALLEL DATA INPUTS (in this case A and C are HIGH and B and D are LOW) is loaded into the register and is present at the QA-QD outputs. During this operation the S1 MODE INPUT is taken LOW; this is the control setting for SHIFT RIGHT operation. This has no effect during the clock pulse cycle as the data transfer is effected during the positive-going edge of the clock pulse only.

At the next positive to negative edge of the clock pulse a shift right data transfer takes place in the register as follows:

QA goes LOW, because at the time of the edge the SHIFT RIGHT SERIAL data input was LOW (though after the edge it goes HIGH and thus has no effect):

QB takes the HIGH state that was present on QA.

QC takes the LOW state that was present on QB.

QD takes the HIGH state that was present on QC.

Thus all the bits are shifted one bit to the right in the individual registers.

This shift right action can be followed in the waveform diagrams for the remaining time allocated to the shift right mode of operation. Because the serial data input has been made LOW, then at the end of this mode's cycle all the outputs are LOW.

S0 is then made LOW and S1 made HIGH to prepare the register for SHIFT LEFT operation.

On the next positive edge of the clock, as the SHIFT LEFT DATA input is LOW then all the outputs remain LOW. However, before the next positive edge this input changes from LOW to HIGH.

The next positive edge changes the output QD to the HIGH state present on the shift left data input. During this clock pulse cycle this input changes from HIGH to LOW.

The next positive edge of the clock changes:

QD to the LOW state present at the input, and

QC to the HIGH state that was present on QD.

This SHIFT LEFT action can be followed in the waveform diagrams for the remaining time allocated to the "SHIFT LEFT" mode of operation.

At the end of the SHIFT LEFT operation both S0 and S1 are taken LOW so that the INHIBIT mode is selected. **No matter what inputs are applied to either of the data inputs** the outputs do not change.

The register is finally cleared again.

(a) To be used as a modem receiver, the shift register will normally need to be able to accept data in serial form and transmit it in parallel form. So the register will have to be initially set to the SHIFT DATA RIGHT (or LEFT, depending on the word to be transmitted) mode to input the word and then to the INHIBIT mode to store the word until the next word is input for transmission.

The sequence of steps is :

(1) CLEAR set to LOW, all outputs are LOW.

(2) S1 is set LOW and S0 is set HIGH, to select the SHIFT RIGHT mode.

(3) CLEAR is then set HIGH.

(The register is now ready to receive data, so that as data arrives it will be clocked into the register. Each time a POSITIVE edge occurs the data present on pin 2 will be stored in QA, and all the other bits shifted to the right.)

It will require the positive-going edge from four clock pulses to load the data word into the register. On completion of the loading of the fourth bit the data is available for reading from the outputs QA-QD. These outputs would normally be isolated from the device requesting this data by either a LATCH or a BUFFER.

The decision whether or not to use buffers is not normally reached until the specification for the device that gives or takes the data to or from the register has been consulted. If this specifies that it has buffered inputs and outputs, then additional buffering is not normally considered necessary. In this example it will be considered that the device receiving the data is not buffered, and hence some form of buffering should be incorporated into the design. This will normally be built into the circuit so that the output of the register is isolated from the device to which it is giving data to. As there are no specific requirements for anything more than a device that will be isolated from the bus until a data word has been read into the register, then the extra cost of a latch cannot be justified and an ordinary buffer with tri-state outputs to isolate the transmitter from the receiving device can be used. The 74125/6 are described as :

Quad 3-state buffers (active high or low (respectively) enable). The choice of device will be determined solely by whether HIGH or LOW enable is required; this will present no interfacing problems with the shift register. The ENABLE input can be activated by the external peripheral when data from the register is required.

(c) Use as a modem transmitter will require the data to be input in parallel form and output in serial form. Therefore PARALLEL LOAD is initially required with pins 9 and 10 HIGH, while the data is loaded into the register; and then either SHIFT DATA RIGHT or SHIFT DATA LEFT to transmit the data in serial form.

The sequence of steps is as follows:

(1) A 4-bit data word applied to pins 3 - 6 (the parallel inputs A-D).

(2) Mode 1 is selected, so that the data can be output in shift-right serial form.

(3) Four clock pulses are applied and the serial output taken from QD.

Q 2.5

For an SN74151A explain:

(a) The function of the device.

(b) Using a simplified diagram how it works as a multiplexer (MUX).

(c) Also device circuits that will enable it to be used as an 8-input multiplexer, and a parallel-to-serial converter.

A.2.5

(a) In figure 2.5.1 the 74151 is described as an 8-input multiplexer. This means that from 8 separate inputs of data one can be selected for output.

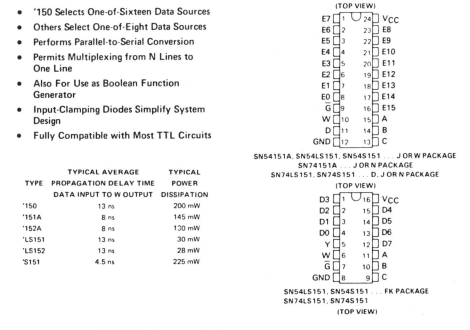

- '150 Selects One-of-Sixteen Data Sources
- Others Select One-of-Eight Data Sources
- Performs Parallel-to-Serial Conversion
- Permits Multiplexing from N Lines to One Line
- Also For Use as Boolean Function Generator
- Input-Clamping Diodes Simplify System Design
- Fully Compatible with Most TTL Circuits

TYPE	TYPICAL AVERAGE PROPAGATION DELAY TIME DATA INPUT TO W OUTPUT	TYPICAL POWER DISSIPATION
'150	13 ns	200 mW
'151A	8 ns	145 mW
'152A	8 ns	130 mW
'LS151	13 ns	30 mW
'LS152	13 ns	28 mW
'S151	4.5 ns	225 mW

Figure 2.5.1 SN74151A general information

(b) The multiplexer operates as a digitally controlled 8-position switch, the code presented to the SELECT input controlling which of the inputs is connected to the output. Figure 2.5.2 shows the basic operation

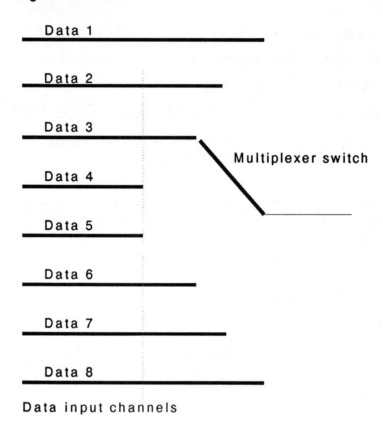

Data 1

Data 2

Data 3

Multiplexer switch

Data 4

Data 5

Data 6

Data 7

Data 8

Data input channels

Figure 2.5.2 Basic operation of a multiplexer

of a MUX. (The switch is, in fact, not a rotary switch at all, but 8, 4-input AND gates which operate in the same way as a rotary switch.) As drawn, the switch is connected so that the input on pin 1 is connected to the output. The signals present on the select input are able to select and connect other inputs through to the output.

(c) Pins 1-4 and 12-15 are the 8-input lines and are designated I0-I7.

Pins 9, 10, and 11 are the SELECT inputs, the selection of the input line being decided by the signals applied to the select inputs. There are three such inputs and hence 8 possible combinations of connections.

Each combination will uniquely switch one of the 8 inputs to the output.

Pins 5 and 6 are the outputs, pin 6 giving the inverted output available from pin 5.

Pin 7 is the STROBE input, the enable for the output is ACTIVE-LOW.

Pin 16 is V_{CC} and pin 8 ground.

The truth table for the selection of inputs is given in figure 2.5.3. This shows that with the STROBE input LOW, then the combination of signals present on the SELECT input selects the input line that is to be connected to the output. The binary number represented by the signals present on A, B and C directly selects the equivalent decimal line. So when A = B = C = LOW, the equivalent decimal number is 0 and so D0 is selected as the input data line that is connected to the output. When the select signals are such as in penultimate line of the truth table, and have

INPUTS				OUTPUTS	
SELECT			STROBE	Y	W
C	B	A	$\overline{G}$		
X	X	X	H	L	H
L	L	L	L	D0	$\overline{D0}$
L	L	H	L	D1	$\overline{D1}$
L	H	L	L	D2	$\overline{D2}$
L	H	H	L	D3	$\overline{D3}$
H	L	L	L	D4	$\overline{D4}$
H	L	H	L	D5	$\overline{D5}$
H	H	L	L	D6	$\overline{D6}$
H	H	H	L	D7	$\overline{D7}$

H = high level, L = low level, X = irrelevant

Figure 2.5.3 Truth table for the selection of inputs

a decimal equivalent of 6, then D6 is selected and connected to the output.

The switching characteristics in figure 2.5.4 show that the maximum propagation delay is 38 ns, this occurring when a new input line is switched to the output; the shortest maximum time is 14 ns for a change on the selected data line to appear as a change at the output.

To operate as an 8-input multiplexer, it is necessary to provide the device with the correct signals to enable the multiplexing to take place. It will normally be part of a data system and hence the STROBE and

SELECT signals will normally be provided by the system itself under the overall control of a master clock. This clock decides the sequence in which lines are to be multiplexed. In these cases, therefore, decisions are made external to the device, and assuming that the control signals are of the correct polarity, then nothing more is required than connecting the device in circuit.

PARAMETER¶	FROM (INPUT)	TO (OUTPUT)	TEST CONDITIONS	'150 MIN	'150 TYP	'150 MAX	'151A, '152A MIN	'151A, '152A TYP	'151A, '152A MAX	UNIT
t_{PLH}	A, B, or C (4 levels)	Y						25	38	ns
t_{PHL}	A, B, or C (4 levels)	Y						25	38	ns
t_{PLH}	A, B, C, or D (3 levels)	W			23	35		17	26	ns
t_{PHL}	A, B, C, or D (3 levels)	W			22	33		19	30	ns
t_{PLH}	Strobe $\overline{G}$	Y	$C_L = 15\,pF$, $R_L = 400\,\Omega$, See Note 4					21	33	ns
t_{PHL}	Strobe $\overline{G}$	Y						22	33	ns
t_{PLH}	Strobe $\overline{G}$	W		15.5		24		14	21	ns
t_{PHL}	Strobe $\overline{G}$	W		21		30		15	23	ns
t_{PLH}	D0 thru D7	Y						13	20	ns
t_{PHL}	D0 thru D7	Y						18	27	ns
t_{PLH}	E0 thru E15, or D0 thru D7	W		8.5		14		8	14	ns
t_{PHL}	E0 thru E15, or D0 thru D7	W		13		20		8	14	ns

¶ t_{PLH} = propagation delay time, low-to-high level output
t_{PHL} = propagation delay time, high-to-low level output

Figure 2.5.4 Switching characteristics

To be used as a parallel-serial converter will require the SELECT input to sequence through the data inputs. Normally this device will be part of a data system and hence may well be externally controlled .

A HILO simulation of its action is given in figure 2.5.5. As there are no external inputs applied to the circuit an 8-bit binary counter has been used in this simulation to supply the clock pulses.

```
SIMULATE PISO
 *TYP
 *

2 OF  SN72LS112A
1 OF  SN74LS151
PISO LOADED OK
```

	C K	I7	I6	I5	I4	I3	I2	I1	I0	S2	S1	S0	OUT	
--TIME--														
0	0	0	0	0	0	1	1	1	1	0	0	0	0	
31	0	0	0	0	0	1	1	1	1	0	0	0	1	BIT0
100	1	0	0	0	0	1	1	1	1	0	0	0	1	
200	0	0	0	0	0	1	1	1	1	0	0	0	1	
214	0	0	0	0	0	1	1	1	1	0	0	1	1	BIT1
300	1	0	0	0	0	1	1	1	1	0	0	1	1	
400	0	0	0	0	0	1	1	1	1	0	0	1	1	
414	0	0	0	0	0	1	1	1	1	0	0	0	1	
430	0	0	0	0	0	1	1	1	1	0	1	0	1	BIT2
500	1	0	0	0	0	1	1	1	1	0	1	0	1	
600	0	0	0	0	0	1	1	1	1	0	1	0	1	
614	0	0	0	0	0	1	1	1	1	0	1	1	1	BIT3
700	1	0	0	0	0	1	1	1	1	0	1	1	1	
800	0	0	0	0	0	1	1	1	1	0	1	1	1	
816	0	0	0	0	0	1	1	1	1	0	1	0	1	
832	0	0	0	0	0	1	1	1	1	0	0	0	1	
846	0	0	0	0	0	1	1	1	1	1	0	0	1	
877	0	0	0	0	0	1	1	1	1	1	0	0	0	BIT4
900	1	0	0	0	0	1	1	1	1	1	0	0	0	
1000	0	0	0	0	0	1	1	1	1	1	0	0	0	
1014	0	0	0	0	0	1	1	1	1	1	0	1	0	BIT5
1100	1	0	0	0	0	1	1	1	1	1	0	1	0	
1200	0	0	0	0	0	1	1	1	1	1	0	1	0	
1216	0	0	0	0	0	1	1	1	1	1	0	0	0	
1230	0	0	0	0	0	1	1	1	1	1	1	0	0	BIT6
1300	1	0	0	0	0	1	1	1	1	1	1	0	0	
1400	0	0	0	0	0	1	1	1	1	1	1	0	0	
1414	0	0	0	0	0	1	1	1	1	1	1	1	0	BIT7
1500	1	0	0	0	0	1	1	1	1	1	1	1	0	
1600	0	0	0	0	0	1	1	1	1	1	1	1	0	
1616	0	0	0	0	0	1	1	1	1	1	1	0	0	
1632	0	0	0	0	0	1	1	1	1	1	0	0	0	
1648	0	0	0	0	0	1	1	1	1	0	0	0	0	
1679	0	0	0	0	0	1	1	1	1	0	0	0	1	BIT0

Figure 2.5.5 HILO simulation of an 8-input MUX

Q.2.6

Explain using a manufacturers' data book how an SN74143 could form part of a digital counter.

A.2.6

This device is termed a "4-BIT COUNTER-LATCH,SEVEN-SEGMENT LED/LAMP DRIVER". It is packaged in a 24-pin package and contains the equivalent of 86 gates on a single chip; the inputs are buffered. The maximum clock frequency is 18 MHz and the power dissipation is 280 mW. It is cascadable so that a counter can be made having any required number of digits.

The function table in figure 2.6.1 is large and it is profitable to look at the penultimate column, TYPICAL DISPLAY, as well as at the inputs in order to discover how the input signals affect the output. Scanning directly from the column headed CLOCK PULSE to the DISPLAY column shows in lines 3-12, how the clock pulses are related to the output display. For these lines (3-12) it is only necessary to arrange the remaining inputs as shown in the inputs column for the basic counter to work.

Line 1 shows the input conditions for clearing the counter to 0 and also for blanking the display.

Line 2 shows how the display may be blanked off using the BLANKING INPUT facility on pin 5.

Lines 3-12 have been described above but it should be noted that the MAXIMUM COUNT OUTPUT pin 22 goes LOW in line 12 when the digital display is 9. The applications data in figure 2.6.2 shows how this output from the LSB counter is used to feed the PARALLEL COUNT ENABLE INPUTS of the other counters; this inhibits the other counters until the counter returns to 0.

Line 13 has the CLOCK PULSE COUNT at 0 but the DISPLAY column shows an 8. NOTE C however says the RIPPLE BLANKING INPUT must be HIGH to display a zero.

Lines 14-18 continue with the count.

FUNCTION TABLE

FUNCTION	CLOCK PULSE	CLEAR	LATCH STROBE	RBI	BI	DECIMAL INPUT	SERIAL CARRY	PARALLEL CARRY	RBI/RBO	MAXIMUM COUNT OUTPUT	QD	QC	QB	QA	a	b	c	d	e	f	g	dp	TYPICAL DISPLAY	NOTES
Clear Ripple Blank		L	L	L	X	X	X	X	L	H	L	L	L	L	OFF	OFF	OFF	OFF	OFF	OFF	OFF	OFF	blank	A
Blank		H	L	X	H	X	X	X	L	H	L	L	L	L	OFF	OFF	OFF	OFF	OFF	OFF	OFF	OFF	blank	A, D
Decimal	0	H	L	H	L	H	L	L	H	H	L	L	L	H	ON	ON	ON	ON	ON	ON	OFF	ON	0.	B
	1	H	L	H	L	L	L	L	H	H	L	L	L	H	OFF	ON	ON	OFF	OFF	OFF	OFF	OFF	1	B
	2	H	L	H	L	L	L	L	H	H	L	L	H	L	ON	ON	OFF	ON	ON	OFF	ON	OFF	2	B
	3	H	L	H	L	L	L	L	H	H	L	L	H	H	ON	ON	ON	ON	OFF	OFF	ON	OFF	3	B
	4	H	L	H	L	L	L	L	H	H	L	H	L	L	OFF	ON	ON	OFF	OFF	ON	ON	OFF	4	B
	5	H	L	H	L	L	L	L	H	H	L	H	L	H	ON	OFF	ON	ON	OFF	ON	ON	OFF	5	B
	6	H	L	H	L	L	L	L	H	H	L	H	H	L	ON	OFF	ON	ON	ON	ON	ON	OFF	6	B
	7	H	L	H	L	L	L	L	H	H	L	H	H	H	ON	ON	ON	OFF	OFF	OFF	OFF	OFF	7	B
	8	H	L	H	L	L	L	L	H	H	H	L	L	L	ON	ON	ON	ON	ON	ON	ON	OFF	8	B
	9	H	L	H	L	L	L	L	H	L	H	L	L	H	ON	ON	ON	ON	OFF	ON	ON	OFF	9	B, C
	0	H	L	H	L	L	L	L	H	H	L	L	L	H	ON	ON	ON	ON	ON	ON	OFF	OFF	0	B
	1	H	L	H	L	L	L	L	H	H	L	L	L	H	OFF	ON	ON	OFF	OFF	OFF	OFF	OFF	1	B
	2	H	L	H	L	L	L	L	H	H	L	L	H	L	ON	ON	OFF	ON	ON	OFF	ON	OFF	2	B
	3	H	L	H	L	L	L	L	H	H	L	L	H	H	ON	ON	ON	ON	OFF	OFF	ON	OFF	3	B
	4	H	L	H	L	L	L	L	H	H	L	H	L	L	OFF	ON	ON	OFF	OFF	ON	ON	OFF	4	B
	5	H	L	H	L	L	L	L	H	H	L	H	L	H	ON	OFF	ON	ON	OFF	ON	ON	OFF	5	B
Latch	6	H	H	H	L	L	L	L	H	H	L	H	H	L	ON	OFF	ON	ON	ON	ON	ON	OFF	6	B
Latch	7	H	H	H	L	L	L	L	H	H	L	H	H	H	ON	ON	ON	OFF	OFF	OFF	OFF	OFF	7	B
	8	H	L	H	L	L	L	L	H	H	H	L	L	L	ON	ON	ON	ON	ON	ON	ON	OFF	8	B
	9	H	L	H	L	L	L	L	H	L	H	L	L	H	ON	ON	ON	ON	OFF	ON	ON	OFF	9	B
Ripple Blank	0	H	L	H	X	L	L	L	L	H	L	L	L	H	OFF	OFF	OFF	OFF	OFF	OFF	OFF	OFF	None	A, B, E

NOTES:
A. RBI/RBO is wire-AND logic serving as ripple blanking input (RBI) and/or ripple blanking output (RBO).
B. The blanking input (BI) must be low when functions DECIMAL/0 through 20/RIPPLE BLANK are desired.
C. The ripple blanking input (RBI) must be open or high to display a zero during the decimal 0 input.
D. When a high logic level is applied directly to the blanking input (BI) all segment outputs are off regardless of any other input condition.
E. When the ripple-blanking input (RBI) and outputs QA through QD are at a low logic level, all segment outputs are off and the ripple-blanking output (RBO) goes to a low logic level (response condition).

SEGMENT IDENTIFICATION

Figure 2.6.1 SN74143 function table

This application demonstrates how the drivers may be cascaded for N-bit display applications. It features:

Synchronous, look-ahead counting
Ripple blanking of leading zeros; blanking of trailing zeros (not illustrated) can also be implemented
Overriding blanking for total suppression or intensity modulation of display
Direct parallel clear
Latch strobe permits counter to acquire next display while viewing current display

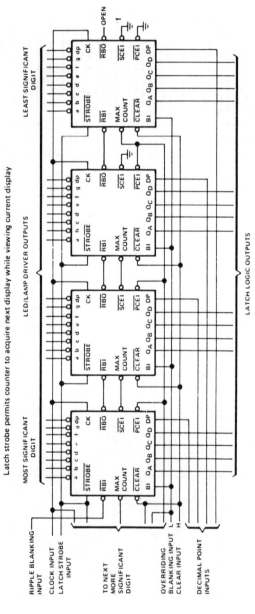

Figure 2.6.2 SN74143 typical application data

Functions of the inputs and outputs of these devices are as follows:

FUNCTION	PIN NO.	DESCRIPTION
CLEAR INPUT	3	When low, resets and holds counter at 0. Must be high for normal counting.
CLOCK INPUT	2	Each positive-going transition will increment the counter provided that the circuit is in the normal counting mode (serial and parallel count enable inputs low, clear input high).
PARALLEL COUNT ENABLE INPUT (PCEI)	23	Must be low for normal counting mode. When high, counter will be inhibited. Logic level must not be changed when the clock is low.
SERIAL COUNT ENABLE INPUT (SCEI)	1	Must be low for normal counting mode, also must be low to enable maximum count output to go low. When high, counter will be inhibited and maximum count output will be driven high. Logic level must not be changed when the clock is low.
MAXIMUM COUNT OUTPUT	22	Will go low when the counter is at 9 and serial count enable input is low. Will return high when the counter changes to 0 and will remain high during counts 1 through 8. Will remain high (inhibited) as long as serial count enable input is high.
LATCH STROBE INPUT	21	When low, data in latches follow the data in the counter. When high, the data in the latches are held constant, and the counter may be operated independently.
LATCH OUTPUTS (Q_A, Q_B, Q_C, Q_D)	17, 18, 19, 20	The BCD data that drives the decoder can be stored in the 4-bit latch and is available at these outputs for driving other logic and/or processors. The binary weights of the outputs are: $Q_A = 1$, $Q_B = 2$, $Q_C = 4$, $Q_D = 8$.
DECIMAL POINT INPUT	7	Must be high to display decimal point. The decimal point is not displayed when this input is low or when the display is blanked.
BLANKING INPUT ($\overline{BI}$)	5	When high, will blank (turn off) the entire display and force $\overline{RBO}$ low. Must be low for normal display. May be pulsed to implement intensity control of the display.
RIPPLE-BLANKING INPUT ($\overline{RBI}$)	4	When the data in the latches is BCD 0, a low input will blank the entire display and force the $\overline{RBO}$ low. This input has no effect if the data in the latches is other than 0.
RIPPLE-BLANKING OUTPUT ($\overline{RBO}$)	6	Supplies ripple blanking information for the ripple blanking input of the next decade. Provides a low if $\overline{BI}$ is high, or if $\overline{RBI}$ is low and the data in the latches in BCD 0; otherwise, this output is high. This pin has a resistive pull-up circuit suitable for performing a wire-AND function with any open-collector output. Whenever this pin is low the entire display will be blanked; therefore, this pin may be used as an active-low blanking input.
LED/LAMP DRIVER OUTPUTS (a, b, c, d, e, f, g, dp)	15, 16, 14, 9 11, 10, 13, 8	Outputs for driving seven-segment LED's or lamps and their decimal points. See segment identification and resultant displays on following page.

SEGMENT IDENTIFICATION

NUMERICAL DESIGNATIONS—RESULTANT DISPLAYS

0   1   2   3   4   5   6   7   8   9

Figure 2.6.3 Applications data

Line 19 shows the effect of the LATCH facility. On the previous line (18), STROBE INPUT was changed from its normal LOW to a HIGH. The LATCH OUTPUTS QA-QD remain with outputs as they did in the previous line i.e. binary 5. The display however, is showing the correct clock pulse count. This state continues in line 20 where the display is 7 but the latches remain as before at binary 5.

Line 21 shows that when the LATCH is taken LOW again the LATCH OUTPUTS have the same value as the display.

The remaining inputs required to construct a counter are shown in figure 2.6.3. Decisions as to the function of the counter will affect many of the inputs; pin 8, for example is the DP (decimal point input) depending on whether the decimal point is required at all. If it is required; will its position be switched with an external range switch? This will determine the inputs needed in conjunction with the function table.

Q.2.7

Counter circuits can be constructed using MSI devices. Use a manufacturer's data sheet to design the following counters:

(a) Divide-by-5 unweighted, using an SN7490A.

(b) Divide-by-8 ripple counter, using an SN7493A.

(c) Divide-by-15 synchronous counter, using an SN74161A, explaining the features of each device.

A.2.7

A catalogue entry for MSI counter ICs is shown in figure 2.7.1.

(a) The 7490A is a decade counter, and a 7493 is a 4-bit binary counter; their descriptions and pin outs are shown in figure 2.7.2, and their count sequence and reset/count function tables are shown in figure 2.7.3.

The power connections for the 7490A is not standard, using pin 5 for V_{CC} and pin 10 for 0 V; the actual power consumption is 145 mW. Two reset lines are provided, RO(1) and RO(2); as well as two lines designated R9(1) and R9(2). The function of these lines can be seen

TTL Counters

	STD	LS	ALS	
Decade up	X	X		7490
Divide-by twelve		X		7492
4-bit binary	X	X		7393
BCD asynchronous		X		74160
Binary asynchronous	X	X	X	74161

Figure 2.7.1 A catalogue entry for TTL counters

'90A, 'LS90 . . . DECADE COUNTERS

'92A, 'LS92 . . . DIVIDE-BY-TWELVE
COUNTERS

'93A, 'LS93 . . . 4-BIT BINARY
COUNTERS

TYPES	TYPICAL POWER DISSIPATION
'90A	145 mW
'LS90	45 mW
'92A, '93A	130 mW
'LS92, 'LS93	45 mW

description

Each of these monolithic counters contains four master-slave flip-flops and additional gating to provide a divide-by-two counter and a three-stage binary counter for which the count cycle length is divide-by-five for the '90A, and 'LS90, divide-by-six for the '92A and 'LS92, and divide-by-eight for the '93A, and 'LS93.

All of these counters have a gated zero reset and the '90A, and 'LS90 also have gated set-to-nine inputs for use in BCD nine's complement applications.

To use their maximum count length (decade, divide-by-twelve, or four-bit binary) of these counters, the CKB input is connected to the Q_A output. The input count pulses are applied to CKA input and the outputs are as described in the appropriate function table. A symmetrical divide-by-ten count can be obtained from the '90A, or 'LS90 counters by connecting the Q_D output to the CKA input and applying the input count to the CKB input which gives a divide-by-ten square wave at output Q_A.

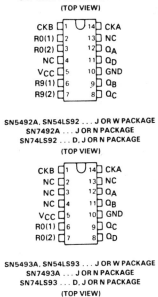

SN5490A, SN54LS90 . . . J OR W PACKAGE
SN7490A . . . J OR N PACKAGE
SN74LS90 . . . D, J OR N PACKAGE
(TOP VIEW)

SN5492A, SN54LS92 . . . J OR W PACKAGE
SN7492A . . . J OR N PACKAGE
SN74LS92 . . . D, J OR N PACKAGE
(TOP VIEW)

SN5493A, SN54LS93 . . . J OR W PACKAGE
SN7493A . . . J OR N PACKAGE
SN74LS93 . . . D, J OR N PACKAGE
(TOP VIEW)

Figure 2.7.2 Counters, general information

'90A, 'LS90
BCD COUNT SEQUENCE
(See Note A)

COUNT	OUTPUT			
	Q_D	Q_C	Q_B	Q_A
0	L	L	L	L
1	L	L	L	H
2	L	L	H	L
3	L	L	H	H
4	L	H	L	L
5	L	H	L	H
6	L	H	H	L
7	L	H	H	H
8	H	L	L	L
9	H	L	L	H

'92A, 'LS92
COUNT SEQUENCE
(See Note C)

COUNT	OUTPUT			
	Q_D	Q_C	Q_B	Q_A
0	L	L	L	L
1	L	L	L	H
2	L	L	H	L
3	L	L	H	H
4	L	H	L	L
5	L	H	L	H
6	H	L	L	L
7	H	L	L	H
8	H	L	H	L
9	H	L	H	H
10	H	H	L	L
11	H	H	L	H

A. Output Q_A is connected to input CKB for BCD count.

C. Output Q_A is connected to input CKB.

Figure 2.7.3 Counters, function tables

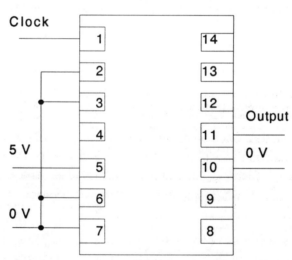

Figure 2.7.4 Divide-by-five counter

from the reset/count function table. There are, in lines 1 and 2, two possible ways in which the counter can be cleared to LOW; both involve taking the R0 inputs HIGH with the R9 inputs LOW. For a count sequence, it can be seen that all the "R"-pins could be held LOW; for both **counting and clearing,** the R(9) pins can both be held LOW; and for **counting,** the R(0) pins should be LOW and taken HIGH when **clearing.** The counter effectively comes in two halves; as the device contains both a divide-by-2 and a divide-by-5. (NOTE for a divide-by-10 counter these two halves must be connected, by joining the second clock input CKB to the output of QA.) As the design calls for a divide-by-5, then only one-half of the counter need be used. It will be seen that QA is the output of the divide-by-2 counter and that QD forms the output of the divide-by-5 counter; the bi-quinary table shows that when the count reaches 4, QD goes HIGH so that QD is the output pin; this output is also used to reset QD to LOW.

Similar features on the 7492 (which is a divide-by-12 counter) allow it to be used as a divide-by-6 counter. It is a counter again constructed in two parts; a divide-by-6 counter and a divide-by-2 counter. The reset/count table shows that to clear the counter, the R0 pins should be HIGH; and for counting LOW, the divide-by-6 output can be seen from the count sequence table to be QD.

Again, for divide-by-12 operation the two parts of the counter would need to be connected together. These requirements are incorporated in the circuit diagram in figure 2.7.5.

(b) The data book entry in figure 2.7.6 for a 74161 describes it as a "synchronous counter with direct Clear". It is a 4-bit counter, and is fully programmable. Clearing the counter is achieved by applying a LOW to the CLEAR input, where regardless of the clock state, the counter is cleared.

The waveforms in figure 2.7.7 show a typical sequence of events, and in this case replace the function or truth table. As this device is cleared asynchronously, the "SYNC CLEAR" pulse input is not relevant to this application. Applying a LOAD pulse is seen to load the data inputs A, B, C and D (which represent binary-12) into QA-QD respectively. For all these functions the ENP and ENT lines are held LOW and while the normal count proceeds they are taken HIGH. The RCO (CARRY OUT) line goes HIGH at the count of 15, and then the count resumes at 0.

If there is no requirement to be able to pre-load the counter, pins 3-6 can all be grounded and the LOAD command at count-15 will load the counter with 0, presetting it, as the synchronous setting action requires a LOW input on the LOAD pin to disable the counter and cause the output to agree with the QA-QD inputs irrespective of the level of the enable inputs, so that both ENT and ENP can be hardwired to V_{CC}. The output will again be from QD. These requirements are incorporated in the circuit diagram in figure 2.7.8.

The switching characteristics of this device are presented in tabular form in figure 2.7.9, and in the form of waveform parameters in figure 2.7.10. This latter diagram shows the clock waveform, the QA-QD output waveforms and the RCO output waveform. The clock waveform shows an amplitude level of 3 V and the width of the clock pulse as t_w between the two voltage reference level. Comparing the clock pulse waveform with the QA waveform it will be seen that there is not an instantaneous change in QA in response to a positive edge from the clock, it is delayed on this LOW to HIGH transition by a time t_{PLH}; the value of this for a 74161 is read from figure 2.7.9 as typically 13 ns with a maximum value of 20 ns. The corresponding HIGH to LOW transition again does not happen simultaneously with the positive edge of the clock pulse but is subject to a propagation delay time of t_{PHL} which is shown on the waveform diagram and can be read from figure 2.7.9 as typically 15 ns with a maximum value of 25 ns. The other Q outputs and RCO have similar delays. After the t_{PHL} transitions the point is marked on the waveform (V_{REF}) to show at which point in the count cycle the transition is measured at, as QA is a divide-by-2, the transition was measured at t_{n+2}, which would be the second clock pulse where QA would toggle from HIGH to LOW.

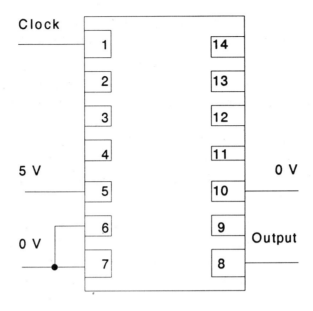

Figur 2.7.5 Divide-by-six circuit diagram

'160,'161,'LS160A,'LS161A . . . SYNCHRONOUS COUNTERS WITH DIRECT CLEAR
'162,'163,'LS162A,'LS163A,'S162,'S163 . . . FULLY SYNCHRONOUS COUNTERS

- Internal Look-Ahead for Fast Counting

- Carry Output for n-Bit Cascading

- Synchronous Counting

- Synchronously Programmable

- Load Control Line

- Diode-Clamped Inputs

SERIES 54', 54LS', 54S' . . . J OR W PACKAGE
SERIES 74' . . . J OR N PACKAGE
SERIES 74LS', 74S' . . . D, J OR N PACKAGE
(TOP VIEW)

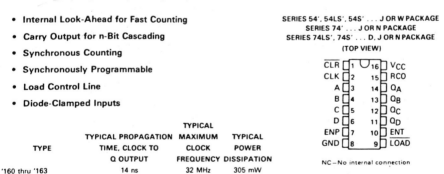

NC – No internal connection

TYPE	TYPICAL PROPAGATION TIME, CLOCK TO Q OUTPUT	TYPICAL MAXIMUM CLOCK FREQUENCY	TYPICAL POWER DISSIPATION
'160 thru '163	14 ns	32 MHz	305 mW
'LS162A thru 'LS163A	14 ns	32 MHz	93 mW
'S162 and 'S163	9 ns	70 MHz	475 mW

Figure 2.7.6 Counters,general information

typical clear, preset, count, and inhibit sequences

Illustrated below is the following sequence:
1. Clear outputs to zero ('161 and 'LS161A are asynchronous; '163, 'LS163A, and 'S163 are synchronous)
2. Preset to binary twelve
3. Count to thirteen, fourteen fifteen, zero, one, and two
4. Inhibit

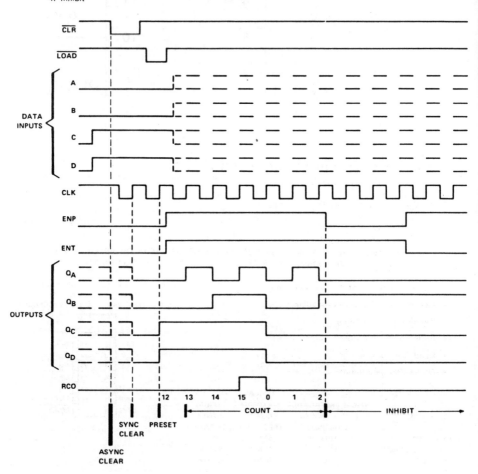

Figure 2.7.7 Waveforms for a 74161

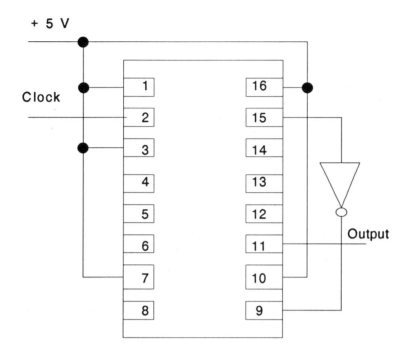

Figure 2.7.8   Divide-by-15 counter using a 74161

PARAMETER¶	FROM (INPUT)	TO (OUTPUT)	TEST CONDITIONS	MIN	TYP	MAX	UNIT
f_{max}				25	32		MHz
t_{PLH}	CLK	RCO			23	35	ns
t_{PHL}					23	35	
t_{PLH}	CLK	Any	$C_L = 15\,pF$,		13	20	ns
t_{PHL}	($\overline{LOAD}$ input high)	Q	$R_L = 400\,\Omega$,		15	23	
t_{PLH}	CLK	Any	See Figures 1 and 2		17	25	ns
t_{PHL}	($\overline{LOAD}$ input low)	Q	and Note 5		19	29	
t_{PLH}	ENT	RCO			11	16	ns
t_{PHL}					11	16	
t_{PHL}	$\overline{CLR}$	Any Q			26	38	ns

¶f_{max} = Maximum clock frequency
t_{PLH} = propagation delay time, low-to-high-level output
t_{PHL} = propagation delay time, high-to-low-level output
NOTE 5:   Propagation delay for clearing is measured from the clear input for the '160 and '161 or from the clock input transition for the '162 and '163.

Figure 2.7.9 Binary counters, switching characteristics

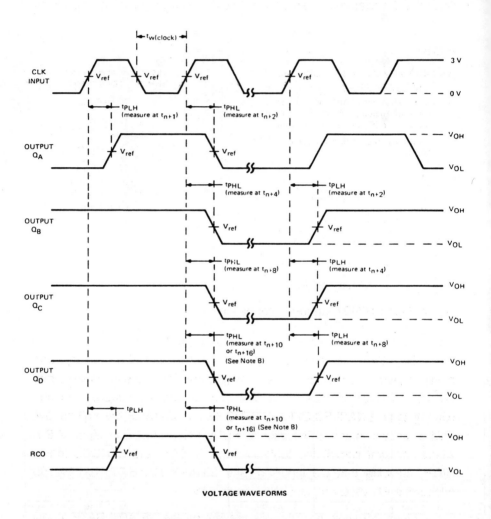

VOLTAGE WAVEFORMS

NOTES: A. The input pulses are supplied by a generator having the following characteristics: PRR ≤ 1 MHz, duty cycle ≤ 50%, Z_{out} ≈ 50 Ω, for '160 thru '163, t_r ≤ 10 ns, t_f ≤ 10 ns; for 'LS160A thru 'LS163A t_r ≤ 15 ns, t_f ≤ 6 ns; and for 'S162, 'S163, t_r ≤ 2.5 ns, t_f ≤ 2.5 ns. Vary PRR to measure f_{max}.
   B. Outputs Q_D and carry are tested at t_{n+10} for '160, '162, 'LS160A, 'LS162A, and 'S162, and at t_{n+16} for '161, '163, 'LS161A, 'LS163A, and 'S163, where t_n is the bit time when all outputs are low.
   C. For '160 thru '163, 'S162, and 'S163, V_{ref} ≈ 1.5 V; for 'LS160A thru 'LS163A, V_{ref} = 1.3 V.

Figure 2.7.10 Binary counters, switching parameters

Q.2.8

Describe the features of an SN7497 device and suggest an application for it.

A.2.8

- Perform Fixed-Rate or Variable-Rate Frequency Division

- For Applications in Arithmetic, Radar, Digital-to-Analog (D/A), Analog-to-Digital (A/D), and other Conversion Operations

- Typical Maximum Clock Frequency . . . 32 Megahertz

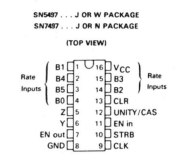

description

These monolithic, fully synchronous, programmable counters utilize Series 54/74 TTL circuitry to achieve 32-megahertz typical maximum operating frequencies. These six-bit serial binary counters feature buffered clock, clear, and enable inputs to control the operation of the counter, and a strobe input to enable or inhibit the rate input/decoding AND-OR-INVERT gates. The outputs have additional gating for cascading and transferring unity-count rates.

Figure 2.8.1 SN7497, general information

The 7497 is described as a synchronous 6-bit binary rate multiplier, which is capable of performing either fixed-rate or variable-rate division up to clock rates of 32 MHz. The inputs are buffered. For the counter to be ENABLED CLEAR, STROBE and ENABLE must all be low. This is shown in the STATE/RATE FUNCTION TABLE in figure 2.8.2, where the first line of the table has the CLEAR and STROBE inputs HIGH, showing that the inputs on the BINARY RATE inputs have no effect. The ENABLE output is HIGH in this case.

Lines 2-9 show how the bits present on the BINARY RATE inputs affect the Y and Z outputs.

When (as in line 2) all the inputs are LOW, then the Z output remains HIGH. When (as in line 4) B1 is HIGH and the remaining binary rate inputs are LOW, then 64 clock pulses at the input will give 2 pulses at the output. The rate of these pulses is related to the clock frequency by the formula contained in figure 2.8.1, so that when only B1 is HIGH M = 2

			INPUTS			OUTPUTS			
			BINARY RATE	NUMBER OF	UNITY/	LOGIC LEVEL OR NUMBER OF PULSES			
CLEAR	ENABLE	STROBE	B5 B4 B3 B2 B1 B0	CLOCK PULSES	CASCADE	Y	Z	ENABLE	NOTES
H	X	H	X X X X X X	X	H	L	H	H	B
L	L	L	L L L L L L	64	H	L	H	1	C
L	L	L	L L L L L H	64	H	1	1	1	C
L	L	L	L L L L H L	64	H	2	2	1	C
L	L	L	L L L H L L	64	H	4	4	1	C
L	L	L	L L H L L L	64	H	8	8	1	C
L	L	L	L H L L L L	64	H	16	16	1	C
L	L	L	H L L L L L	64	H	32	32	1	C
L	L	L	H H H H H H	64	H	63	63	1	C
L	L	L	H H H H H H	64	L	H	63	1	D
L	L	L	H L H L L L	64	H	40	40	1	E

NOTES: A. H = high level, L = low level, X = irrelevant. All remaining entries are numeric counts.

B. This is a simplified illustration of the clear function. The states of clock and strobe can affect the logic level of Y and Z. A low unity/cascade will cause output Y to remain high.

C. Each rate illustrated assumes a constant value at rate inputs; however, these illustrations in no way prohibit variable-rate inputs.

D. Unity/cascade is used to inhibit output Y.

E. $f_{out} = \dfrac{M \cdot f_{in}}{64} = \dfrac{(8 + 32) f_{in}}{64} = \dfrac{40 f_{in}}{64} = 0.625 \, f_{in}$

Figure 2.8.2 SN7479, state and function table

and f_{out} = half of the input frequency. In line 11 where B5 = B3 = HIGH, the resulting multiplier is 0.625. By suitable choice of signals on B1-B5 the multiplying factor can be altered in steps of 0.015625 x f_{in}.

Q.2.9

A keyboard-switch encoder is required for data entry of 16 bits from an RS 337-100 low profile keyboard. Describe how this encoder operates.

A.2.9

Figure 2.9.1 is the block diagram for this device. It shows that the keys forming the keypad are arranged in a 4 x 4 matrix, such that X4 and Y4 correspond to F hex or 15 decimal, and X3 and Y2 correspond to 6. This arrangement of switches into columns and rows is a typical feature of keyboards and is similar to the arrangement in memory cells. A clock input is required together with an input signal from the controlling device to enable the tri-state outputs. The output signals consist of a DATA AVAILABLE signal and the 4-bit binary representation of the key which has been selected, with bit A being the LSB and bit D the MSB.

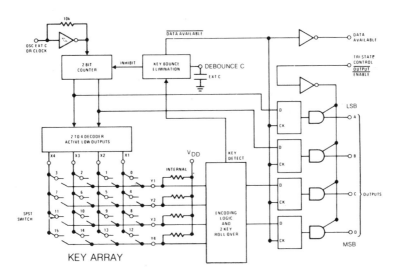

Figure 2.9.1 Keyboard encoder, block diagram

Figure 2.9.2 shows the switching times and the delays associated with them. Here it can be seen that to change from a logic level to a high-Z state on the tri-state outputs can take a maximum of 200 ns with V_{DD} = 5 V to a maximum of 110 ns when V_{DD} is increased to 15 V. The waveforms on the right-hand side of the data sheet show the points from which the time is measured. The debouncing period of the switches is shown by the oscillations at the start and finish of the KEY waveforms; from these waveforms it can be seen that DATA AVAILABLE goes HIGH after the first key is pressed and then, after waiting for the switch debounce period, goes HIGH again to indicate that another key has been pressed. The tri-state outputs are low power Schottky compatible, as well as being CMOS compatible.

When a key is pressed there is a delay T_1 before the DATA AVAILABLE line goes HIGH. Then after the "Propagation Delay Time" (which can vary from a minimum of 25 ns when V_{DD} = 15 V to a maximum of 150 ns when V_{DD} = 5 V), the data word is available for output. An OUTPUT ENABLE input from the controlling device is then required to activate the output tri-state devices.

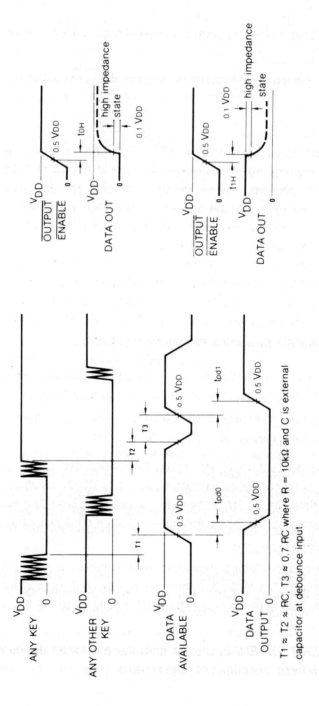

T1 ≈ T2 ≈ RC, T3 ≈ 0.7 RC where R = 10kΩ and C is external capacitor at debounce input.

Figure 2.9.2 Keyboard encoder, switching waveforms

Q.2.10

(a) Explain using a block diagram the internal organisation of a 1K x 4-bit RAM.

(b) Show how such a RAM could be used in the construction of a 3K x 8-bit RAM.

A.2.10

(a) The block diagram of a 1K x 4-bit RAM is shown in figure 2.10.1. The memory array is arranged to provide a total of 1024 x 4 = 4096 storage locations. These storage locations are arranged in 16 columns and 64 rows, so that to select any particular location to either write data into or to read data from, will involve selecting that location via the correct combination of row and column.

The address bus would require 4 bits to be used to decode the column and 6 bits to decode the row. There would also be a requirement for a 4-bit data bus. These address and data lines are A0-A5 for the row select, A6-A9 for the column select, and D1-D4 for the data bus. There are two additional inputs which are normally present:

CS is a CHIP ENABLE input which alerts the device to the fact that either a READ or a WRITE function is to be performed on it.

WE is the READ/WRITE control input; this will be HIGH for one of the functions and LOW for the other.

(b) To be capable of storing an 8-bit word, two of the 4-bit ICs would need to be connected in parallel, data bits D0-D3 being applied to one IC and data bits D4-D7 to the other. CS and WE would be applied to both ICs making up the 8-bit combination. Such a configuration is shown in figure 2.10.2.

To extend this 8-bit combination to 3K would then require three of the 8-bit circuits. Figure 2.10.3 shows a typical configuration for 3K of 8-bit memory built from 4-bit ICs. The parallel combination of ICs are A, B and C to give the 8-bit word.

The CHIP ENABLE inputs are derived via a 74LS139A dual 2-line to 4-line address decoder, its input being from address bus lines

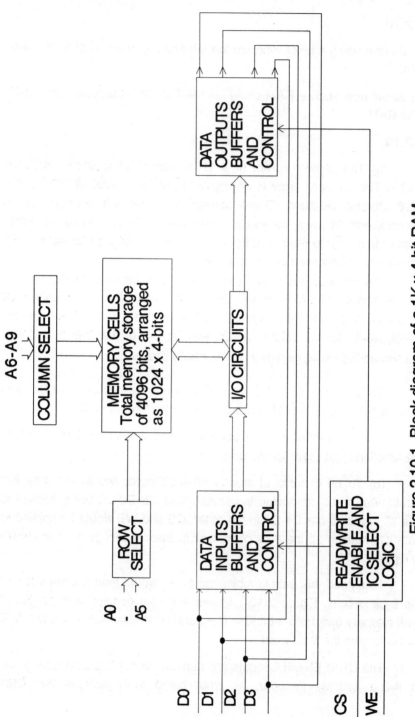

Figure 2.10.1 Block diagram of a 1K x 4-bit RAM

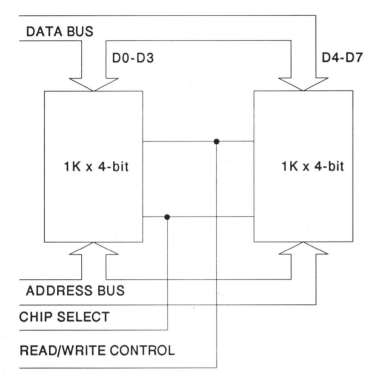

DATA BUS

D0-D3

D4-D7

1K x 4-bit

1K x 4-bit

ADDRESS BUS

CHIP SELECT

READ/WRITE CONTROL

Figure 2.10.2 An 8-bit memory system constructed from 4-bit ICs

A10-A11. The address bus lines A0-A9 are directly connected to each of
the ICs. A particular pair of ICs will be enabled by decoding the address
bits present at the input of the address decoder. The logic diagram and
function table for the 74LS139A are given in figure 2.10.4. It can be seen
that only one of the four outputs is LOW at any one time, this output
being selected from the combination of input signals present on pins 2
and 3 which in this case is derived from the address bus lines A10 and
A11 (for this application only one of the dual devices is required). Thus
only one of the three pairs of memory ICs will be enabled for read or
write sequences.

(NOTE. This technique is applicable to the construction of
READ/WRITE memories of any size that can be accommodated within
the constraints of the address and data buses. There are also many

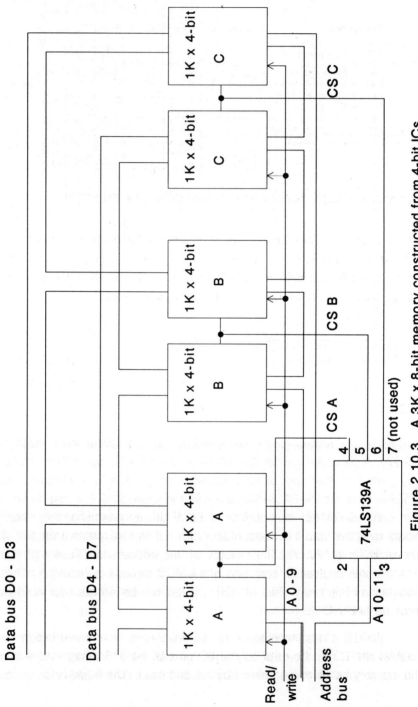

Figure 2.10.3   A 3K x 8-bit memory constructed from 4-bit ICs

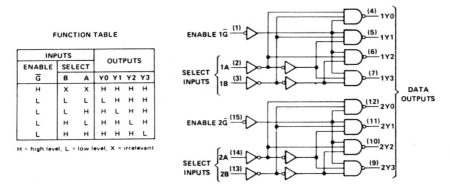

FUNCTION TABLE

INPUTS		OUTPUTS			
ENABLE	SELECT				
$\overline{G}$	B	A	Y0	Y1	Y2	Y3

ENABLE	SELECT		OUTPUTS			
$\overline{G}$	B	A	Y0	Y1	Y2	Y3
H	X	X	H	H	H	H
L	L	L	L	H	H	H
L	L	H	H	L	H	H
L	H	L	H	H	L	H
L	H	H	H	H	H	L

H = high level, L = low level, X = irrelevant

Figure 2.10.4 Logic diagram and function table for a 74LS139A

available commercial memory boards which are designed to be used with CPU-specific system ICs to ease a system designer's task. The description and analysis of such devices is more specific for a book on microcomputers technology, and is not dealt with here.)

Q.2.11

Explain, using a data sheet, the operation as a RAM of the CYM1421 device.

A.2.11

The CYM1421 is a 1 Mbit static RAM. It is organised as 128K words by 8 bits, and it consists of four 32K x 8 bit static rams arranged as shown in figure 2.11.1. The outputs of this device are TTL compatible while the device itself is fabricated with CMOS technology having a power dissipation of 600 mW. The 1421HD-70 version has shorter access times than the 1421HD-85 version.

WRITE is accomplished when both CS (chip select) and WE (write enable) are LOW, the data on the I/O pins I/O0-I/O16 being written into the memory locations addressed by the address inputs A0-A16.

READ is accomplished when both CS and OE (output enable) are LOW and WE is high, again the address and data being present as for the WRITE command.

The table of switching characteristics in figure 2.11.2 and the switching waveforms in figure 2.11.3 together show how the access time of 70 ns for t_{ACS} is derived. t_{ACS} is quoted for the two versions as 70 ns and 85 ns during the read cycle. These times are derived from the time CS goes LOW, (followed by OE going LOW) until the data on the I/O pins is valid. In both the tables and the waveforms it can be seen that the time for OE going low until the data is valid is seen as less than the time for a response to CS going low. The ADDRESS set-up time is also 70 or 85 ns, so that when all the command lines are asserted at the same time there is no delay waiting for a slow response. The other switching characteristics can obtained by relating the table with the relevant waveforms.

When the WRITE cycle is controlled by the WE command then the waveforms in figure 2.11.4 apply. The ADDRESS and CE lines are asserted first and once an address location has been selected then WE is marked. The WE pulse needs to have a minimum value of 30-35 ns during which time the DATA IN is valid and is written into the addressed memory location. The WRITE cycle time is the same as the READ cycle time.

Maximum Ratings

(Above which the useful life may be impaired)

Storage Temperature . . . . -65°C to +150°C

Ambient Temperature with
Power Applied . . . . -55°C to +125°C

Supply Voltage to Ground Potential . . . . -0.3V to +7.0V

DC Voltage Applied to Outputs
in High Z State . . . . -0.3V to +7.0V

DC Input Voltage . . . . -0.3V to +7.0V

Output Current into Outputs (Low) . . . . 50 mA

Operating Range

Range	Ambient Temperature	V$_{CC}$
Commercial	0°C to +70°C	5V ± 10%
Military	-55°C to +125°C	5V ± 10%

Electrical Characteristics Over Operating Range

Parameters	Description	Test Conditions	CYM1421HD Min.	CYM1421HD Max.	Units
V$_{OH}$	Output HIGH Voltage	V$_{CC}$ = Min., I$_{OH}$ = -1.0 mA	2.4		V
V$_{OL}$	Output LOW Voltage	V$_{CC}$ = Min., I$_{OL}$ = 4.0 mA		0.4	V
V$_{IH}$	Input HIGH Voltage		2.2	V$_{CC}$	V
V$_{IL}$	Input LOW Voltage		-0.3	0.8	V
I$_{IX}$	Input Load Current	GND ≤ V$_I$ ≤ V$_{CC}$	-10	+10	μA
I$_{OZ}$	Output Leakage Current	GND ≤ V$_O$ ≤ V$_{CC}$. Output Disabled	-10	+10	μA
I$_{CC}$	V$_{CC}$ Operating Supply Current	V$_{CC}$ = Max., I$_{OUT}$ = 0 mA $\overline{CS}$ = V$_{IL}$		120	mA
I$_{SB_1}$	Automatic $\overline{CS}$ [2] Power Down Current	Max. V$_{CC}$, $\overline{CS}$ ≥ V$_{IH}$. Min. Duty Cycle = 100%		70	mA
I$_{SB_2}$	Automatic $\overline{CS}$ [2] Power Down Current	Max. V$_{CC}$, $\overline{CS}$ ≥ V$_{CC}$ - 0.2V, V$_{IN}$ ≥ V$_{CC}$ - 0.2V or V$_{IN}$ ≤ 0.2V		20	mA

Capacitance[3]

Parameters	Description	Test Conditions	Max.	Units
C$_{IN}$	Input Capacitance	T$_A$ = 25°C, f = 1 MHz V$_{CC}$ = 5.0V	35	pF
C$_{OUT}$	Output Capacitance		40	pF

Notes:

1. Not more than 1 output should be shorted at one time. Duration of the short circuit should not exceed 30 seconds.

2. A pull-up resistor to V$_{CC}$ on the $\overline{CS}$ input is required to keep the device deselected during V$_{CC}$ power-up, otherwise I$_{SB}$ will exceed values given.

3. Tested on a sample basis.

AC Test Loads and Waveforms

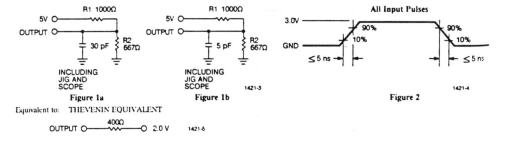

Figure 1a   Figure 1b   Figure 2

Equivalent to: THEVENIN EQUIVALENT

Figure 2.11.1 CYM 1421 general information

Switching Characteristics Over Operating Range [4]

Parameters	Description	1421HD-70		1421HD-85		Units
		Min.	Max.	Min.	Max.	
READ CYCLE						
t_{RC}	Read Cycle Time	70		85		ns
t_{AA}	Address to Data Valid		70		85	ns
t_{OHA}	Data Hold from Address Change	5		5		ns
t_{ACS}	$\overline{CS}$ LOW to Data Valid		70		85	ns
t_{DOE}	$\overline{OE}$ LOW to Data Valid		40		50	ns
t_{LZOE}	$\overline{OE}$ LOW to LOW Z	5		5		ns
t_{HZOE}	$\overline{OE}$ HIGH to HIGH Z		30		35	ns
t_{LZCS}	$\overline{CS}$ LOW to Low Z [6]	5		5		ns
t_{HZCS}	$\overline{CS}$ HIGH to High Z [5, 6]		35		35	ns
WRITE CYCLE [7]						
t_{WC}	Write Cycle Time	70		85		ns
t_{SCS}	$\overline{CS}$ LOW to Write End	65		75		ns
t_{AW}	Address Set-up to Write End	65		75		ns
t_{HA}	Address Hold from Write End	10		15		ns
t_{SA}	Address Set-up to Write Start	25		25		ns
t_{PWE}	$\overline{WE}$ Pulse Width	30		35		ns
t_{SD}	Data Set-up to Write End	20		20		ns
t_{HD}	Data Hold from Write End	10		10		ns
t_{LZWE}	$\overline{WE}$ LOW to Low Z [6]	5		5		ns
t_{HZWE}	$\overline{WE}$ HIGH to High Z [5, 6]	0	45	0	50	ns

Notes:

4. Test conditions assume signal transition times of 5 ns or less, timing reference levels of 1.5V, input levels of 0 to 3.0V and output loading of the specified I_{OL} / I_{OH} and 30 pF load capacitance.

5. t_{HZCS} and t_{HZWE} are specified with C_L = 5 pF as in *Figure 1b*. Transition is measured ±500 mV from steady state voltage.

6. At any given temperature and voltage condition, t_{HZCS} is less than t_{LZCS} for any given device. These parameters are guaranteed and not 100% tested.

7. The internal write time of the memory is defined by the overlap of $\overline{CS}$ LOW and $\overline{WE}$ LOW. Both signals must be LOW to initiate a write and either signal can terminate a write by going HIGH. The data input setup and hold timing should be referenced to the rising edge of the signal that terminates the write.

8. $\overline{WE}$ is HIGH for read cycle.

9. Device is continuously selected, $\overline{CS}$ = V_{IL} and $\overline{OE}$ = V_{IL}.

10. Address valid prior to or coincident with $\overline{CS}$ transition low.

11. Data I/O will be high impedance if $\overline{OE}$ = V_{IH}.

Figure 2.11.2 CYM 1421 switching characteristics

Switching Waveforms[10]

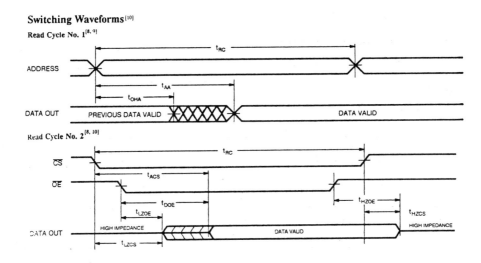

Figure2.11.3 CYM 1421 read cycle

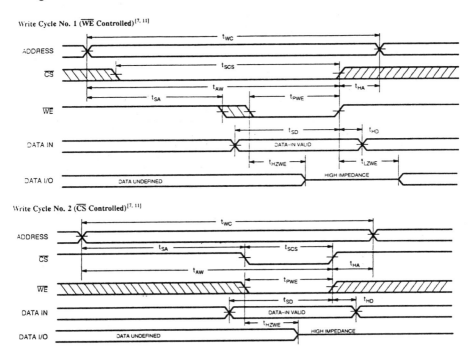

Note: If $\overline{CS}$ goes HIGH simultaneously with $\overline{WE}$ HIGH, the output remains in a high impedance state.

Figure 2.11.4 CYM 1421 write cycle

Q.2.12 Library assignment

What are the differences between PROMs, LOGIC ARRAYS and ASICs? Discuss advantages and disadvantages for these types.

A.2.12

PROM stands for Programmable Read Only Memory. There are many types of PROM; these can be classified into those types which are bought ready programmed as in a microcomputer and those which can be programmed by the user (PROMs). These latter categories can be subdivided into those types which can have their contents altered (EPROMs) and those which cannot. The former type may for example have their contents erased by either ultra violet light (UV EPROMs) or electrically (EAROMs). In use in a circuit, then, the PROMs will require additional circuitry to identify which memory element is to be read, and to control the flow of information with respect to timing. The basic PROM consists of an input, decoder which is configured with AND gates and a programmable OR matrix. With this configuration it is possible to connect every output with every input. These devices are highly suited to storing bit patterns, such as look-up tables and for storing the character set for a VDU.

Logic arrays are another family of devices which, like the PROM, are programmed by the user, normally by blowing a fusible link. (In both cases, quite sophisticated hardware and software could be required to program the IC.) Whereas a PROM is a programmable memory device, a logic array is a programmable LOGIC device. The layout internally is similar to the PROM in that there are an input AND array and an output OR array, but now it is the AND array which can be programmed, **not** the OR array. A typical basic array structure is shown in figure 2.12.1. The pads allow external connections to be made to the array.

The array is constructed from AND and OR gates. The method of representing the gates differs somewhat from the normal method due to the fact that there are far more gates in the array than in a normal IC. Figure 2.12.2 shows how a 3-input AND gate is shown on a circuit diagram for an array. The vertical lines are the input lines and the horizontal line is often called the product line. The input connections to

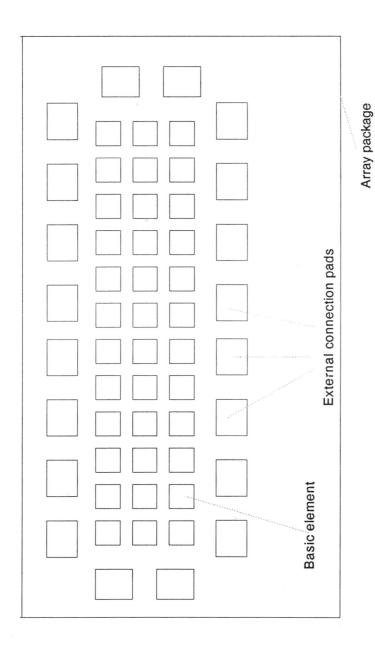

Figure 2.12.1 Basic arrangement of a logic array

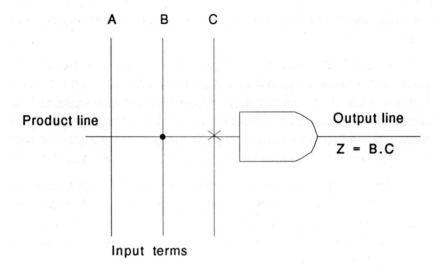

Figure 2.12.2   The representation of a 3-input AND gate used in an array

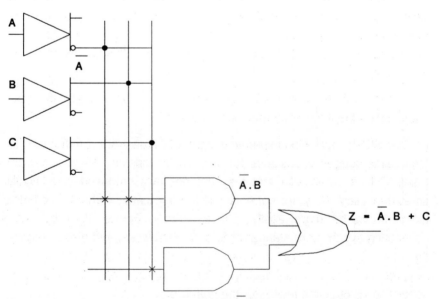

Figure 2.12.3   Implementation of C + Ā.B, using a logic array

the AND gate are made at the junctions of the product line and the input lines.

Figure 2.12.2 also shows how a blown fuse link (so that no connection is made at that point), and a hard-wired connection are made; and how a star (*) is used to indicate connections between inputs and the product line. The function in this figure is F= B.C. When an entire gate has a star marked in its **circuit diagram symbol** it means that the gate has no blown fuses, and therefore it has no effect on the output OR gate.

Figure 2.12.3 also shows how the solution to Q.1.5 is implemented using an array. The inputs A, B and C are fed to the inter-connection matrix through buffers, that have an output of both the function and its NOT form. These are then combined to satisfy the Boolean equation and presented to an output OR gate.

Figure 2.12.4 shows the logic diagram for a TIBPAL16L8 logic array. The fact that the product and input lines are numbered means that any fuse can be identified. The product and input lines are selected during the programming mode and the fuses are blown as required.

The number of inputs that can be connected to the output is limited. There is also available a logic array which has fully programm-able input and output arrays. At the moment this is the most versatile of the range of arrays but is not normally required for uses which are not very complex.

Where there is no need to connect together every output and input combination the logic array may offer advantages.

ASICs (Applications specific integrated circuits) are ICs that are (as their name suggests) designed for a particular function. They differ from other IC logic devices in that they are normally produced in relatively small quantities. They are normally used in applications where a complex function can be more easily realised in one device, than by inter-connecting two or more standard LSI or VLSI devices, and also to reduce the cost, size and power dissipation. The design of an ASIC normally requires the use of CAD packages for the design, and the necessary specialised production facility for the final ICs.

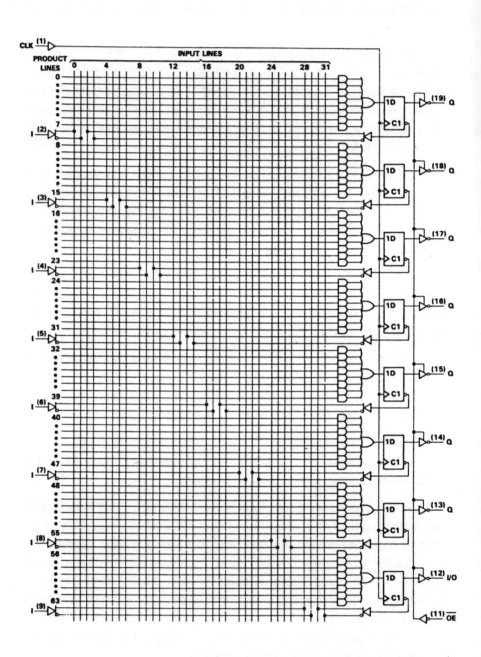

Figure 2.12.4 Logic diagram of a TIBPAL16LB logic array

One disadvantage has already been discussed for both PROMs and logic arrays, namely that as they are both programmable devices they require the hardware and software in order to either program them, or to configure them, in all but the most primitive applications. This equipment is not cheap to purchase and it also may not be used much in low volume applications. Facilities do exist for these devices to be programmed by manufacturers' agents and various hardware/software houses.

The greatest advantage of using any of these types of IC is firstly an improvement in reliability, and also a reduction in both chip count and size of PC board required. Several logic functions can be put into one IC, and the resulting saving in space and weight could be critical factors in a design. Both PROMs and undedicated arrays are available as a standard range of products (an ASIC would of course need to specifically produced for an application). This means that once the internal structure of the device is decided it can be relatively easily produced. Where a modification is required as a result of user feedback, an upgrading or retrofit then may be accomplished by simply replacing one programmable or ASIC device with another of newly developed internal structure.

3 System Design

3.1 Prior Knowledge

You should be familiar with the following aspects of Karnaugh mapping:

(a) The structure of the map and the relevance of each square in it.

(b) The method of inserting states into, and reading groups from the map.

(c) The basic properties of J-K flip-flops and synchronous and asynchronous counters.

A review question on these topics is contained in **Q.1.5** and **Q.1.7.**

3.2 Introduction

This chapter looks at the tools used to design digital circuits. In particular it will look at how state diagrams and Karnaugh maps can be used in designing synchronous and asynchronous systems.

Design requires more than simply producing a circuit either on a piece of paper or on a bread-board that meets a given specification. It involves **documentation**. A well documented design is one that can be understood by others; it must contain not only the circuit diagram, but also an outline of what the system does, what its inputs are to achieve specific outputs, the waveforms at any test points and any special features with respect to its operation. The documentation should help others to understand the circuit so that its uses and applications are clear.

Designing and building on the basis of a few words of explanation and badly produced diagrams is unacceptable. With this in mind the most useful accessory to the designer of any circuit is a notebook. This does not mean one that is kept in copperplate hand writing, or has every diagram produced by stencils and rulers or by a CAD package. It should be a book that shows how every decision was reached, where your source material was found (e.g. which data sheet or which application note you consulted), what tests were carried out, under what conditions, with what equipment and what the results were.

When the design is complete it is often very useful to simulate the circuit design using either HI-LO or SPICE. This enables the design to be evaluated with a variety of signal inputs and the results to be analysed before construction begins.

The circuit can now be constructed, usually on either a bread-board, designer board or on one of the varieties of perforated strip board.

Having built the circuit, the next stage is to test it. To do this it is necessary to produce (and record in a notebook) a test schedule detailing what tests are to be carried out, with what test equipment and to specify the test signals required. The test specification produced should enable anyone to test the circuit and also demonstrate that the circuit does meet the criteria given.

This aspect of testing is well illustrated, and its importance reinforced, by looking into a manufacturer's data book on logic devices. Here they frequently give a circuit diagram showing how the test equipment used was connected, and under what conditions the test was carried out. That is so if it were ever necessary to repeat the test or to carry out a similar test under different conditions of loading or temperature, information is immediately available.

Q.3.1

(a) Explain what a **present state/next state diagram** is, and use the truth table for a J-K flip-flop to construct a present state/next state diagram showing the transitions in a J-K flip-flop.

(b) From the present state/next state diagram in Q.3.1(a) obtain an alternative form of the diagram showing how a required output state can be obtained by having the correct J or K input.

(c) Explain what a **state transition diagram** is and why it is useful. Use the present state/next state diagram in Q.3.1(a) to obtain the state transition diagram for a J-K flip-flop.

A.3.1

A present state/next state diagram shows the relationship between the present state of a system, the external inputs and the next state.

The columns in figure 3.1.1 are the value of the inputs and the rows are the present state of the system. The individual cells in the diagram are the next state that the system will go to after a clock pulse.

The truth table for a J-K flip-flop is shown in figure 3.1.2. The

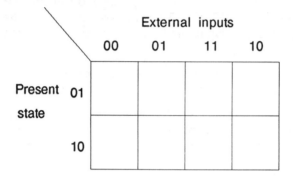

Figure 3.1.1   Empty present state/next state diagram for a J-K flip-flop

columns J and K are the inputs to the flip-flop and the columns Q_n and Q_{n+1} show respectively the output of the flip-flop before and after a clock pulse cycle. 1 and 0 refer to logic levels being HIGH and LOW respectively. It can be seen that no matter what the

J	K	Q_n	Q_{n+1}	
0	0	0	0	No change
0	0	1	1	
1	0	1	1	Set to 1
1	0	0	1	
0	1	1	0	Reset to 0
0	1	0	0	
1	1	1	0	Toggle
1	1	0	1	

Figure 3.1.2 Truth table for a J-K flip-flop

current state is for the flip-flop, when 00 is applied at the input there is no change at the output. This can be plotted on the diagram and is shown in figure 3.1.3. Similarly, from the truth table it can be seen that when the input is 01 then the J-K is reset to a zero no matter what the current state of the flip-flop is. This is shown in figure 3.1.4.

Similar arguments allow the cells for the other inputs to be plotted; the completed present state/next state diagram is shown in figure 3.1.5.

(b) From the present state/next state diagram it can be seen that to produce a 0 at the output of the flip-flop after a clock pulse, when the present output is a 0, requires the J-input to be a 0; it does not matter

	External inputs			
	00	01	11	10
Present 01	01			
state 10	10			

Figure 3.1.3 Present state/next state diagram for the input 00

	External inputs			
	00	01	11	10
Present 01		01		
state 10		01		

Figure 3.1.4 Present state/next state diagram for the input 01

what the K-input is. The cells that contain this information have been highlighted in figure 3.1.6.

	External inputs			
	00	01	11	10
Present **01**	01	01	10	10
state				
10	10	01	01	10

Figure 3.1.5 Present state/next state diagram for J-K flip-flop

To output a 1 after a clock pulse cycle when the present output is a 0 requires that the J-input is a 1; again, it does not matter what the K-input is. The cells that contain this information have been highlighted in figure 3.1.7.

Information can be obtained for the "no change" and the "toggle"

	External inputs			
	00	01	11	10
Present **01**	01	01	10	10
state				
10	10	01	01	10

Figure 3.1.6   Present state/next state diagram showing the cells used when the output of 0 is required from a J-K   flip-flop

states; the completed present state/next state diagram is shown in figure 3.1.7.

All four transition states are shown in figure 3.1.8. This figure shows the input states required for a J-K flip-flop for **any** output. For any of the four outputs only one of the inputs has a specified input as either a 1 or a 0, the other input can be either a 1 or a 0.

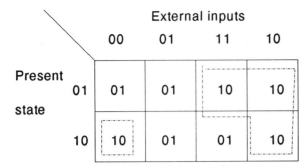

Figure 3.1.7 Present state/next state diagram showing the cells used when the output of 1 is required from a J-K flip-flop

(c) A state transition diagram is used to show graphically a sequential digital system. As with the present state/next state diagram, it shows how the present state of a system changes to the next state depending on the input that is present when a clock pulse is applied.

Q_n	Q_{n+1}	J	K
0	0	0	X
0	1	1	X
1	0	X	1
1	1	X	0

Figure 3.1.8 The transition state table for a J-K flip-flop

The state diagram contains **nodes**, which represent the current states of the system and connecting lines, which are marked with the inputs that will cause the transition from the present state to the next state. Every line showing these state changes must begin and end in a node; when the next state is the same as the present state, then the line will both start and finish in the same node. Figure 3.1.9 (a) shows a node

Q which represents the present state of 0. Figure 3.1.9 (b) shows how that node would respond to the J and K inputs being both at 0, shown by the "00" on the line. The J-K remains at 0 and this is shown by adding "/0" after the "00".

If the input were 10 (which is the SET state for a J-K), then the system would change from 0 to 1, the line showing this change being marked with 10/1. This is shown in figure 3.1.10.

Similar arguments allow the other state transitions to be marked on the diagram, and the completed state transition diagram is shown in figure 3.1.11.

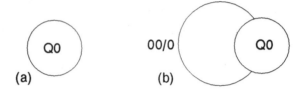

Figure 3.1.9 (a) Node at state Q0; (b) node showing the response to an input of 00

When the next state is different from the present state then the line will finish in a different node from the one it began at.

Figure 3.1.10   State diagram showing the change from Q0 to Q1 resulting from an input of 10

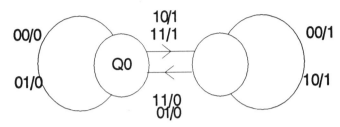

Figure 3.1.11 State diagram for a J-K flip-flop

Q.3.2

(a) Construct a table showing all states of a modulo-8 counter using three J-K flip-flops; from this obtain both a state transition diagram and a state transition table for the counter, and explain their significance.

(b) Beginning with the output at 000, derive state transition diagrams and tables for a modulo-6 counter. From these use Karnaugh maps to design such a counter and simulate its action using HI-LO.

A.3.2

(a) Three J-K flip-flops connected as shown in figure 3.2.1 would form a modulo-8 synchronous counter.

In the state diagram of figure 3.2.2, S0, S1 etc. refer to the number of the clock pulse and also to the numbers of the state (this is simply a convenience to allow positive identification of any state and is arbitrary in the numbering of the states). Q_0, Q_1 etc. refer to the outputs of the flip-flops.

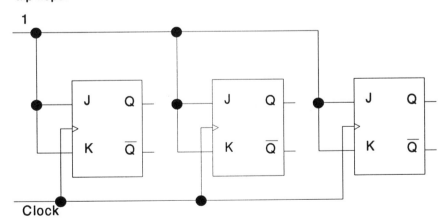

Figure 3.2.1 Mod-8 synchronous counter

State	Q2	Q1	Q0
S0	0	0	0
S1	0	0	1
S2	0	1	0
S3	0	1	1
S4	1	0	0
S5	1	0	1
S6	1	1	0
S7	1	1	1

Figure 3.2.2   A state diagram for a mod-8 counter

A state transition diagram shows how under a train of clock pulses the counter will change from its present state to future states. The changes in state are internally generated as a result of the circuit's interconnections between the individual flip-flops and the clock pulse cycle. It will not in this case matter at which point the cycle of changes is entered, the generation of the next state is automatic. The state transition diagram is shown in figure 3.2.3.

From this diagram, a state transition table can be drawn. This table shows how the counter progresses from its present state to the next state; it is derived from the state transition diagram. From the state table it can be seen that the counter is completely cyclic, going from its present state to the next in an ordered sequence. This is reflected in the state table of figure 3.2.4.

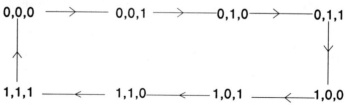

Figure 3.2.3   State transition diagram for a mod-8 counter

State	Present state			Next state		
	Q2	Q1	Q0	Q2	Q!	Q0
S0	0	0	0	0	0	1
S1	0	0	1	0	1	0
S2	0	1	0	0	1	1
S3	0	1	1	1	0	0
S4	1	0	0	1	0	1
S5	1	0	1	1	1	0
S6	1	1	0	1	1	1
S7	1	1	1	0	0	0

Figure 3.2.4 Transition table for a mod-8 counter

(b) For a modulo-6 counter with the count beginning at 000, the first six states (S0 to S5 inclusive) from the state transition table of the mod-8 counter will be required; these are shown in figure 3.2.5. The state

State	Q2	Q1	Q0
S0	0	0	0
S1	0	0	1
S2	0	1	0
S3	0	1	1
S4	1	0	0
S5	1	0	1

Figure 3.2.5 A state diagram for a mod-6 counter

transition diagram can then be similarly modified to exclude the state changes S6 and S7. After S5 the counter will change back to S0; this is shown in figure 3.2.6.

Present state			Next state		
Q2	Q1	Q0	Q2	Q1	Q0
0	0	0	0	0	1
0	0	1	0	1	0
0	1	0	0	1	1
0	1	1	1	0	0
1	0	0	1	0	1
1	0	1	0	0	0

Figure 3.2.6 Transition table for a mod-6 counter

From these diagrams and figure 3.1.8 the Karnaugh maps can be drawn and minimised.

In state S0 the outputs of the three flip-flops are at 000; for state S1, the output required is 001.This requires flip-flop 1 to change its Q0 output from a 0 to a 1, and Q1 and Q2 to remain at 0. From figure 3.2 it is seen that to do this requires flip-flop 1's J-input to be at 1 and the K-inputs at X (the don't care state), and flip-flops 2 and 3 to have their J-input at 0, while their K-inputs are at X.

These results are plotted on the Karnaugh maps. Six maps are needed, one for each of the J and K inputs.

As there is no requirement for the states corresponding to outputs of 1,1,0 and 1,1,1 ; X-s may be added in those squares as well. These are all shown in figure 3.2.7.

The state change from S1 to S2 will require a change from 001 to 010, so that Q1 must change from 0 to 1 and Q0 from 1 to 0, while Q2 remains at 0. This will require K0 to be at 0 while J0 is at X. To change Q1 from 0 to 1 will require J1 at 1 and K1 at X. For Q2 to remain at 0 will require J2 to remain at 0 with K2 at X.

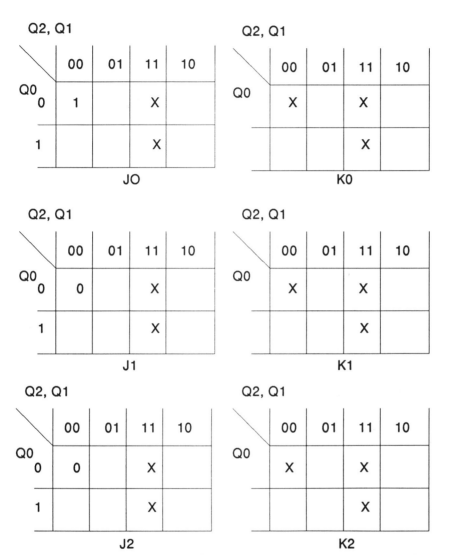

Figure 3.2.7 Karnaugh map for a mod-6 counter, showing the first cell with the inputs

These results are plotted on the Karnaugh maps, and are shown in figure 3.2.8.

The remaining points are plotted in a similar way, and are shown in figure 3.2.9.

JO and KO have only cells corresponding to a 1 input, so these inputs can be connected directly to a 1.

Q2, Q1

Q0 \	00	01	11	10
0	1		X	
1	X		X	

JO

Q2, Q1

Q0 \	00	01	11	10
	X		X	
	1		X	

K0

Q2, Q1

Q0 \	00	01	11	10
0	0		X	
1	1		X	

J1

Q2, Q1

Q0 \	00	01	11	10
	X		X	
	X		X	

K1

Q2, Q1

Q0 \	00	01	11	10
0	0		X	
1	0		X	

J2

Q2, Q1

Q0 \	00	01	11	10
	X		X	
	X		X	

K2

Figure 3.2.8 Karnaugh map for a mod-6 counter (continued), showing the first two cells with their inputs

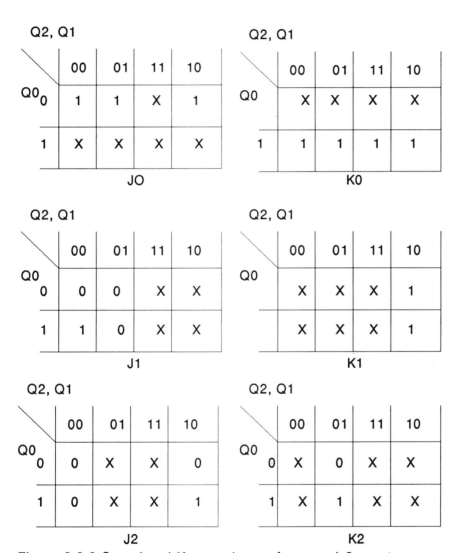

Figure 3.2.9 Completed Karnaugh map for a mod-6 counter

K1 and K2 have cells which correspond directly with Q0, so they will be connected directly to Q0.

J1 has a pattern of 1s and 0s that does not correspond directly with any one input. Figure 3.2.10 shows the states on the inputs for the required output. The truth table relates these states, and shows in the last column the required output. There is no obvious combination of inputs that will produce the required output. If, however the **inverse** of the Q1 and Q2 inputs is "AND-ed" with the Q0 input then the correct output is obtained.

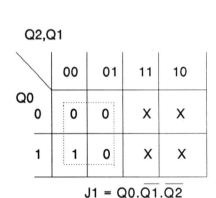

Q0	Q2,Q1	$\overline{Q2},\overline{Q1}$	$\overline{Q2},\overline{Q1},Q0$
0	0,0	1,1	0
1	0,0	1,1	1
0	0,1	1,0	0
1	0,1	1,0	0

$$J1 = Q0.\overline{Q1}.\overline{Q2}$$

Figure 3.2.10 The use of a truth table to obtain the result for J1

Q2, Q1 / Q0 K-map:

	00	01	11	10
0	0	X	X	0
1	0	X	X	1

Q0	Q2,Q1	$\overline{Q2},\overline{Q1}$	$\overline{Q2}.\overline{Q1}.Q0$
0	0,0	1,1	0
1	0,0	1,1	1
0	1,0	0,1	0
1	1,0	0,1	0

$$J2 = Q0.\overline{Q1}.Q2$$

Figure 3.2.11 The use of a truth table to obtain the result for J2

Q2, Q1

	00	01	11	10
Q0 0	1	1	X	1
1	X	X	X	X

JO =1

Q2, Q1

	00	01	11	10
Q0	X	X	X	X
1	1	1	1	1

K0=1

Q2, Q1

	00	01	11	10
Q0 0	0	0	X	X
1	1	0	X	X

$J1 = Q0.\overline{Q1}.\overline{Q2}$

Q2, Q1

	00	01	11	10
Q0	X	X	X	1
	X	X	X	1

K1=K0

Q2, Q1

	00	01	11	10
Q0 0	o	X	X	0
1	0	X	X	1

$J2 = Q0.\overline{Q1}.\overline{Q2}.$

Q2, Q1

	00	01	11	10
Q0 0	X	0	X	X
1	X	1	X	X

K2=Q0

Figure 3.2.12 Completed Karnaugh map for a mod-6 counter showing the necessary inputs

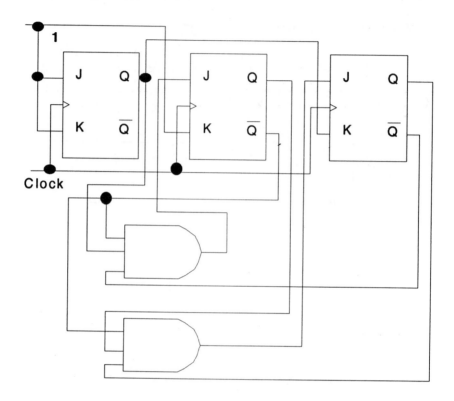

Figure 3.2.13   Mod-6 counter

Similarly for J2, figure 3.2.11 shows only the states for J2, again the use of a truth table shows that there is no obvious combination of inputs that will produce the required output, until the third column is "AND-ed" with the Q0 input.

Figure 3.12.13 shows the required circuit diagram, and figure 3.2.14 the HILO simulation of the circuit.

```
SIMULATE MOD6SIX
 *TYP
 *

3 OF SN72LS112A
1 OF SN74LS11
MODSIX LOADED OK
```

--TIME--	C L K	Q2	Q1	Q0
0	0	0	0	0
100	1	0	0	0
200	0	0	0	0
216	0	0	0	1
300	1	0	0	1
400	0	0	0	1
414	0	0	1	0
500	1	0	1	0
600	0	0	1	0
614	0	0	1	1
700	1	0	1	1
800	0	0	1	1
816	0	1	0	0
900	1	1	0	0
1000	0	1	0	0
1014	0	1	0	1
1100	1	1	0	1
1200	0	1	0	1
1216	0	0	0	0
1300	1	0	0	0

```
FINISH TIME = 1300
```

Figure 3.2.14 HILO simulation of a mod-6 counter

Q.3.3

(a) Many states in counters are not used and are termed "don't care" states. Explain how this can lead to problems.

(b) Design a BCD decade counter in which there is a one step transition from any of the don't care states to 0000.

(c) Explain a disadvantage of this method and suggest an alternative solution to minimise incorrect counting.

A.3.3

(a) A state that is termed as don't care is one that is normally not used, and so should not affect the count. Should a power surge or a glitch of any form occur, then the counter may well find itself in one of these unused states. A mod-34 counter would require six J-K flip-flops with a possible 64 states; 30 of these would be unused. Should a "worst-case" fault occur, then the counter could find itself in count state 35; from here it would need to cycle through the remaining unused states to bring itself to the beginning of the count cycle.

(b) The state transition diagram for such a counter is shown in figure 3.3.1. From this, a transition table can be drawn (figure 3.3.2), which is used to complete the Karnaugh maps.

From this it can be seen that to change from 0000 to 0001 requires the following. For Q0 to change from 0 to 1 requires J0 to be at 1, and for Q1, Q2 and Q3 to remain at 0 requires J1, J2 and J3 to be at 0, all the K-inputs being X. These points and the remaining points are plotted on the Karnaugh maps in figure 3.3.3.

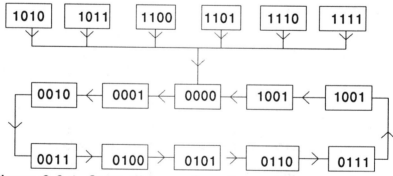

Figure 3.3.1   State diagram for a "one-step-to-zero" transition for a BCD counter

Present state				Next state			
Q3	Q2	Q1	Q0	Q3	Q2	Q1	Q0
0	0	0	0	0	0	0	1
0	0	0	1	0	0	1	0
0	0	1	0	0	0	1	1
0	0	1	1	0	1	0	0
0	1	0	0	0	1	0	1
0	1	0	1	0	1	1	1
0	1	1	1	1	0	0	0
1	0	0	0	1	0	0	1
1	0	0	1	0	0	0	0
1	0	1	0	0	0	0	0
1	0	1	1	0	0	0	0
1	1	0	0	0	0	0	0
1	1	0	1	0	0	0	0
1	1	1	0	0	0	0	0
1	1	1	1	0	0	0	0

Figure 3.3.2 Transition table for a BCD counter with a "one step transition" to zero

(c) In this method the counter is reset to 0000 at the end of the count cycle and also if it is driven into any of the unused states. If the count had reached 0101 when some unwanted event was reached that

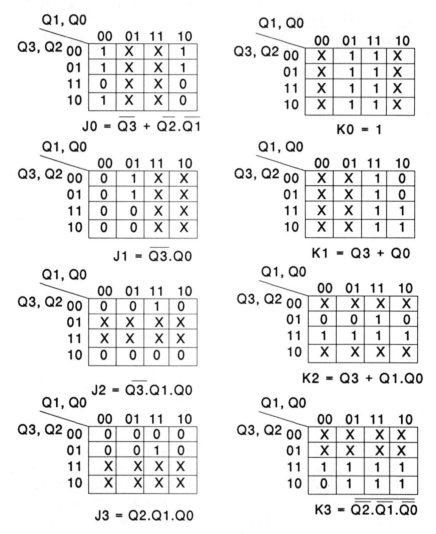

$$JO = \overline{Q3} + \overline{Q2}.\overline{Q1}$$

$$KO = 1$$

$$J1 = \overline{Q3}.Q0$$

$$K1 = Q3 + Q0$$

$$J2 = \overline{Q3}.Q1.Q0$$

$$K2 = Q3 + Q1.Q0$$

$$J3 = Q2.Q1.Q0$$

$$K3 = \overline{\overline{Q2}.\overline{Q1}.\overline{Q0}}$$

Figure 3.3.3 Karnaugh maps for a "one-step transition" to zero BCD counter

drove the counter to 1011, the next clock pulse would reset the counter to 0000; this may not always be desirable.

An alternative system is to cycle the counter in a way that spaces the unused states through the count cycle. Instead of using only the first n-count states and then resetting to 0000, for example, there is no reason why the count should not proceed skipping a certain number of states so as to spread the unused states through the count cycle rather than ignoring the later states only.

Q.3.4

(a) Draw a block diagram of a sequence logic system and use it to explain its action.

(b) Design a sequence detector that will detect the sequence 101 in a train of pulses.

(c) Use a flow diagram to design the sequence detector and explain one advantage of this technique over a state diagram.

A.3.4

(a) Figure 3.4.1 shows a typical sequential logic system, it consists of two basic types of circuit elements:

(i) The **memory** elements which are usually flip-flops, and

(ii) the **logic** elements which are usually combinational circuits.

There are also a clock input and links between the two types of circuits carrying the information about the present and the next state. The input is Y and the output is Z. A sequence detector is designed to give a (normal) 1 output only after a certain pattern of bits has been input at Y; in this case the bit pattern would be 101.

(b) The state diagram for the sequence detector is shown in figure 3.4.2. The initial state of the detector is assumed to be A and it will progress from A to B then to C and finally to state D **when and only when** the input pulses at X have the pattern 101.

If the first pulse applied to the sequence detector is a 0 then the detector will remain at state A; it does not affect the outcome in anyway at all whether state A is either 1 or 0 at the start of the sequence. While it is in state A, the detector is storing the information that the preceding input was not a 1; this is shown by the loop 0/0 around state A.

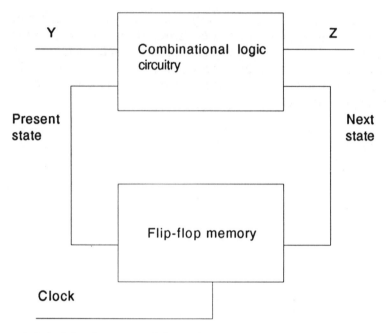

Figure 3.4.1 A basic sequential synchronous system

If however the first pulse is a 1, then this must be stored in the memory of the detector. This is achieved when the state changes from state A to state B.

Whether an input causes the detector to remain in state A or to progress to state B, the output will remain at 0.

In state B there are, of course, two possible inputs to the system. If the input is a 0 then this information will be stored in the system when it changes from state B to state C. If the input is however a 1, it will remain at state B. It will remain here because this input (had the detector been in state A) would cause it to change to B.

If the input when the detector is in state C is a 1, then this is stored by the change to state D. If the input is a 0, then clearly the received bit pattern is not 101 and the detector must change back to its initial state A. This state will change the output from 0 to 1 to indicate that the pattern 101 has been detected.

The next input could be a 0, in which case the next state will be A or it could be 1 in which case the next state will be B.

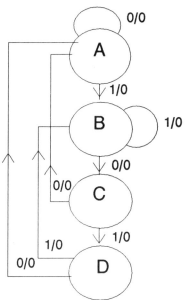

Figure 3.4.2   State diagram for the pattern 101

The complete state diagram can be translated into a state table for all combinations of the input X; this is shown in figure 3.4.3. For two combinations of internal state it is normal to assign the binary values 00 to A, 01 to B, 11 to C and 10 to D. So the state table can be redrawn using these values, and this is shown in figure 3.4.4.

The resulting Karnaugh maps from this table are shown in figure 3.4.5, together with the minimised forms.

The output will only be 1 when the detector is in state C and the next input is a 1. This means that the output will only be 1 when both the Q outputs are 1 and the input is 1.

The resulting circuit diagram is shown in figure 3.4.6.

(c) A flow diagram for the sequence detector is shown in figure 3.4.7. It gives the same information as the state diagram in a different form. At each of the lozenge shaped decision boxes, a question is asked about the bit that has just been input. The result of the question yes or no decides to which point in the flow diagram to move.

This type of diagram is often a neater and less cumbersome way of giving information than the state diagram. With large systems, a state

Present state	Present output Z	Next state	
		Y = 1	Y = 0
A	0	B	A
B	, 0	B	C
C	0	A	D
D	1	A	B

Figure 3.4.3.Sequence detector state table

diagram can often resemble a rat's nest or spaghetti as the number of links to other parts of the diagram is very large.

Present state	Present output Z	Next state	
		Y = 1	Y = 0
00	0	01	00
01	0	01	11
11	0	10	00
10	1	01	00

Figure 3.4.4   Assigned state table

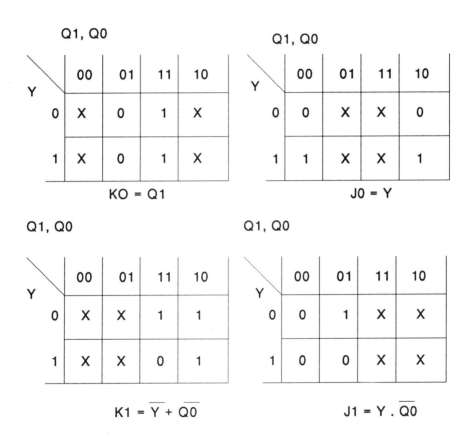

Figure 3.4.5 Karnaugh maps for a 101 sequence detector

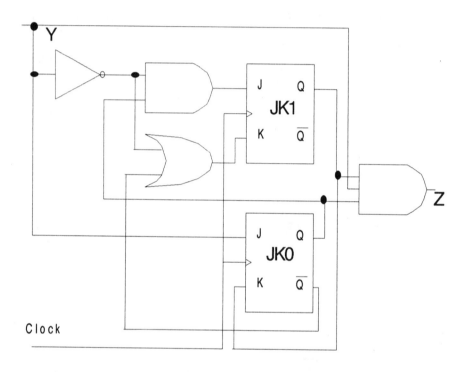

Figure 3.4.6. Circuit diagram for a sequence detector for the pattern 101

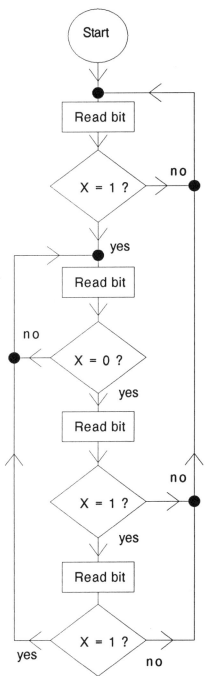

Figure 3.4.7 Flow diagram for a sequence detector for 101

Q3.5

(a) Explain what is meant by the term "static hazard", explain how it occurs and how it can be eliminated in logic circuits.

(b) Explain what is meant by the term "critical race", explain how it occurs and how it can be eliminated in an S-R flip-flop constructed from the NOR gates in a 7402 IC.

A.3.5.

(a) Static hazards occur when changes occur at the output of a logic network as a result of a transition at the input, **when none should occur.**

Static hazards can occur as a result of propagation delays in gates.

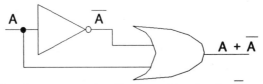

Figure 3.5.1   A circuit to prove the Boolean identity $A + \bar{A} = 1$

Figure 3.5.1 shows a simple circuit built to prove a basic Boolean identity.

One input to the OR gate should always be at 1, and hence the output of the gate should always be at 1. When a change from 1 to 0 occurs at the input that change occurs immediately at the A input of the OR gate. Because of the time it takes the 0 applied to the input of the inverter to propagate through the inverter, the other input of the gate changes from 0 to 1 between 3 and 22 ns later, so that for this period of time both the inputs of the OR gate are at 0; and hence the output of the OR gate will change to 0.

The propagation through a 7404 also takes between 3 and 22 ns.

The timing waveforms are shown in figure 3.5.2.

Static hazards would not occur if there were no propagation delays but as there are such delays in all gates they must be allowed for. This can be done quite simply by adding extra delays in the form of extra gates in the circuit, so that the delays to both inputs of the OR gate have

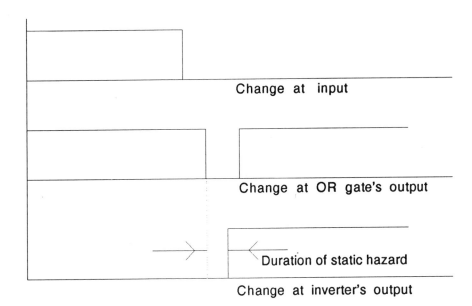

Change at input

Change at OR gate's output

Duration of static hazard

Change at inverter's output

Figure 3.5.2 Timing waveforms for the circuit in 3.5.1 to respond to a
1 to 0 change

approximately the same propagation delay. Figure 3.5.3 shows a
non-inverting buffer in the circuit; if it is also a 74xx device it also
produces a delay of between 3 and 22 ns, and if all the loadings on the
gates are the same will either completely eliminate the hazard or will
reduce the length of the time that the hazard is present.

The Karnaugh map and circuit diagram for a simple but typical
logic circuit is shown figure 3.5.4.

Assume that the input to the gates is:

A = 1

B = 1

C = 1

and that at t = 0 s there is a change in the inputs so that

A = 1

B = 1

C = 0

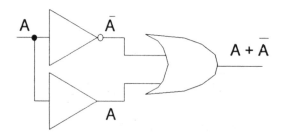

Figure 3.5.3 Non-inverting buffer added to reduce static hazard

Only the value of the C input has changed, the other inputs remain the same.

When C changes from 1 to 0, then the output of gate 1 changes and F1 is now 0. The output of gate 2, F2, changes and is now 1. So to keep the output Z at 1, at least one of its two inputs should remain at 1. The inverted C input for AND gate 2 is derived via an inverter, this will have a propagation delay which will add to the delay caused by the AND gate alone.

For a 7408 quad 2-input AND gate the delay is between 4.5 and 27 ns, and for a 7404 hex inverter it is between 3 ns and 22 ns.

The delay in gate 2 due to both the inverter and the AND gate will be between 7.5 and 49 ns. The delay in gate 1 is clearly between 4.5 and 22 ns.

For a period of between 3.5 and 27 ns the OR gate will have two zeros on its input and will give a 0 output. This will be restored to a 1 when gate 2 gives a 1 output.

This short period of time when the OR gate's output is at 0 may well go unnoticed depending on what the output of the gate is driving: an electromechanical relay would not drop out, a pulse generator driving a triac may produce no faulty triggering; but any digital logic being driven from this output could well have sufficient time to respond, with unforeseeable consequences. One should always be aware of the possibility of a static hazard. Where one might exist and its consequences cause problems, it should be "designed out".

From the Karnaugh map for this circuit, figure 3.5.4, each of the ringed expressions in the dotted boxes represents an AND gate in the actual circuit diagram. When groups are adjacent to each other, then they vary by only one term; when the 1s do not lie in the same group, they are implemented with different AND gates. In the circuit operation just

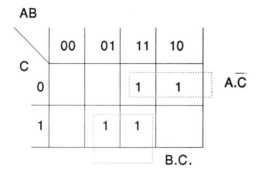

Figure 3.5.4 Karnaugh map for the identity BC + $\overline{\overline{AC}}$

analysed, it was the change in the variable C that caused the outputs of the AND gates to change over. To prevent this change-over from one group to another (or, in a circuit to prevent switching from one AND gate to another) then all the groups will require a group in common. One additional group is then added to the Karnaugh map; this is shown in figure 3.5.5.

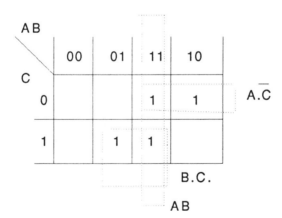

Figure 3.5.5   Modified Karnaugh map with additional AND gate

The extra term will require an additional AND gate and the expression is no longer in its minimal form. However it contains no static hazards. The original set of conditions at the input were

A = 1

B = 1

C = 1

Again at t = 0 s assume that there is a change in the inputs so that

A = 1

B = 1

C = 0

is now input to the circuit.

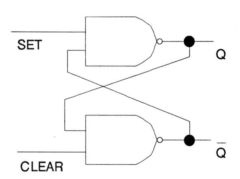

Set	Clear	Output
1	1	No Change
0	1	Q = 1
1	0	Q = 0
0	0	Ambiguous

Figure 3.5.6 S-R flip-flop and truth table

The same changes take place in gates 1 and 2 at the same propagation rates as before **but** gate 3 has both its inputs retained at 1, so its output remains at 1, the OR gate therefore has a 1 present at its input, and so its output remains at 1.

The static hazard has therefore been eliminated.

(b) A 7400 is a quad 2-input NAND IC. When two of the NAND gates are connected as shown in figure 3.5.6, they form an S-R flip-flop; the truth table for the circuit is also given.

When both inputs have a 0 input the outputs will both be at 1; this is illogical as one of the outputs should be the inverse of the other.

When, after this state both inputs are changed back to 1 then the output state will depend on which of the two NAND gates has the lowest propagation delay. If gate A acts faster than gate B, then the 1 at its input will appear at its output faster than at the output of gate B. Hence its output will change first, giving the output state of $Q = 0$. If however the propagation delay in gate B is lower, then its output will change first, making $Q = 1$.

A circuit whose output depends on the propagation delay of the individual gates has race conditions present in it.

4 Transmission of Digital Signals

Q 4.1 Assignment

(a) The RS232C standard is commonly used to transmit data between two devices. There are limits applied to parameters such as the maximum length of cable, maximum rate of data transmission etc.

Relate these parameters to the main factors which can cause degradation to a digital waveform's maximum rate of data transmission etc.

(b) Using ICs intended as RS232C line drivers and receivers, investigate the effect of distortions on the coding and decoding efficiency of these devices. Relate these distortions to the system's specification.

A.4.1

The RS232C interface standard is a specification for the interconnection of active and dumb devices which need to interchange information; such devices could be a computer and a printer. It uses voltage levels which are different from the normal TTL levels; for normal TTL a HIGH is normally at +5 V and a LOW at 0 V. In the RS232C, the voltage level for a 1 is between -5 and -15 V and for a 0 it is between +5 and +15 V.

In the RS232C system there is a trade-off between the rate at which data can be transmitted and the length of cable that can be used to interconnect the two devices that are exchanging data. These limits for the RS232C system are shown in figure 4.1.1.

Hence the longer the interconnecting cable, the slower the rate at which data can be transferred between the two devices. This can be explained by the fact that any cable is made of an electrical conductor (normally copper wire) and some form of insulator (normally PTFE or

118

Baud Rate	Length of cable (ft)
110	2750
300	2500
600	2000
1200	1750
2400	750
4800	500
9600	250
19200	<250

Figure 4.1.1 Baud rates in the RS232 system

PVC). Thus the cable will have some finite value of resistance which will cause some loss of signal amplitude as a signal passes down it. Also present are capacitance and inductance; the capacitance because of the insulator which acts as a dielectric; the inductance because the cable carries a current and forms a current-carrying loop which sets up and links a magnetic field, which is a property of an inductor.

In most lines used to interconnect digital systems it is the capacitance that predominates, and the changing voltage levels on the line have to both charge and discharge the capacitance. The longer the length of cable, the greater the total capacitance presented to the line driver. Over a long transmission path where the total line capacitance is high, or at very high data rates where the rate of change in transmitted signal levels is high, the line capacitance can never be fully either charged or discharged; this causes distortion of the received pulse as shown in figure 4.1.2.

This distortion can cause errors in the line receivers used to convert the RS232C signals back to normal TTL levels. In order to limit the amount of capacitance present in the system the maximum length of cable recommended is 17 m; although this can be increased with good design and the use of low capacitance cables.

With a stream of high-speed pulses there is an additional problem caused by the frequency components present in the pulses. The higher the pulse rate (and hence the shorter the duration of each pulse), the higher the frequency components that are present. These high-frequency components are attenuated more than the lower-frequency components and, as they account for the rapid rise and fall times of the pulses, their

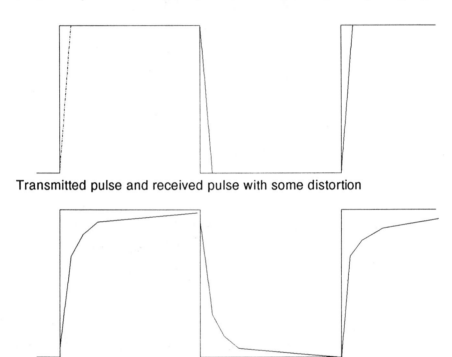

Transmitted pulse and received pulse with some distortion

Transmitted pulse and received pulse with considerable distortion

Figure 4.1.2 The effect of line capacitance on transmitted pulses

attenuation means that these times are increased. As all digital systems require a finite time for a change at the input to produce changes at the output, this distortion can cause malfunction. The various frequency components of the signal propagate through the transmission path at different velocities and so they arrive at the receiver at differing times, and hence are no longer in phase; this again causes distortion of the received pulse. In this system the maximum frequency is 20K baud and the pulse rise and fall times are specified as 30 V/ms. Times in excess of this cause errors.

The RS232C data transmission standard is, by modern standards, a very low-speed system; it is however a well understood one and most of the personal computers sold now have the ability to transfer data in this mode.

The MC1488 and MC1489 ICs are used to change data signal levels between TTL and RS232C standards, the MC1488 acting as a TTL to RS232C converter and the MC1489 acting as an RS232C to TTL converter; the former is called a line driver and the latter a line receiver. Their pin-outs are shown in figure 4.1.3.

Because of the higher voltage levels present in the RS232C system the line driver operates at a supply voltage of plus and minus 12 V; this is the level at which the line receiver receives the signal.

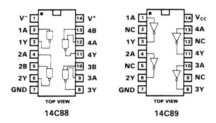

Figure 4.1.3 RS232C line transmitters and receivers

The investigation of the effects of distortion on the line drivers and receivers can be seen by connecting the line receiver to 0 V and +5 V and connecting a detector (LED, DVM or CRO) to an output of one of the gates; to the input of that gate a +12 V dc signal is applied. The voltage present at the output is noted. The dc input voltage is reduced in 0.5 V steps and the state of the output noted; note the voltage level present at the input when the output changes from a 0 to a 1. Reduce the input voltage level to 0 V and note the state of the output; increase the voltage in 0.5 V steps and again monitor the output noting the input voltage level at which the output changes.

Repeat this test with -12 V connected to the input in both an increasing and a decreasing direction, noting again the voltage levels present when the output changes.

Connect a line receiver and transmitter in series via a decade capacitance box with the normal working voltages applied to both the ICs; arrange to monitor the output of line receiver to observe the change from 1 to 0 to 1, and connect a CRO to the input pin of the input gate being used.

With no capacitance present, apply a clock pulse input at a frequency of about 1 kHz to the input of the line transmitter, and sketch the waveform at the input of the receiver, noting particularly the amplitude and the rise and fall times of the clock pulses.

Increase the capacitance in 10 000 pF steps and record the signal waveform received, again paying attention to these three parameters. Continue increasing the capacitance until the receiver fails to decode correctly; sketch the received signal's waveform.

Increase the clock pulse rate to 10 kHz, and then to 100 kHz, and again note the received pulse shapes and amplitudes when correct decoding fails to take place.

These results show that distortion of the received pulse causes incorrect operation of the RS232C transmission path.

The results noted from the laboratory work show that:

(a) Attenuated signals can cause errors; the received signals should exceed 3 V both positive and negative for correct operation.

(b) When too much line capacitance is present, the distorted signals also cause malfunction.

(c) The higher the rate of transmission, the more the signal can be distorted due to both attenuation and line capacitance, and hence the error rate on decoding is higher.

Q.4.2

(a) When signals are distorted malfunction of digital circuits can occur. Simulate using PSPICE the effect of passing a clock pulse train at 200 kHz through a low pass filter consisting of a 100K resistor and a 15 pF capacitor. Obtain both a swept frequency response and a Fourier analysis for this circuit arrangement and discuss the results.

(b) What would be the effect of using such distorted clock pulses to clock a 7473 and a 74112, when they are both used as "divide-by-two" circuits.

A.4.2

The circuit is shown in figure 4.2.1, with the nodes numbered.

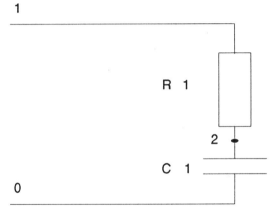

Figure 4.2.1   PSPICE simulation circuit

The circuit description for the swept, transient and Fourier analysis is given in figures 4.2.2(a) and (b).

The transient analysis gives results which cover one clock pulse cycle only, and the Fourier analysis has its results based on the fundamental frequency of 200 kHz. The Fourier decomposition analysis is performed on both the input and output waveforms so that a comparison can be made between harmonic amplitude and phase shift.

The swept frequency response, figure 4.2.3, shows a -3 dB point at 130 kHz, so that some distortion is expected to occur in both the transient and Fourier analysis.

```
*swept response of r-c network
VIN     1         0         AC 6
R1      1         2         100K
C1      2         0         15PF
.AC DEC 10        1KHZ 300KHZ
.PLOT AC VDB(2)
.PROBE
.END

*fourier plot of r-c network
VIN     1         0         PULSE( 0V 5V 0US 0US 0US 2.5US 5US)
R1      1         2         100K
C1      2         0         15PF
-TRAN .001US 5US
.FOUR 200000 V(1) V(2)
.PLOT TRAN V(1) V(2)
.PROBE
.END
```

Figure 4.2.2 PSPICE listings for swept and transient responses

The transient analysis, figure 4.2.4, shows some increase of both the rise and fall times, which is so large that the pulse never reaches its full magnitude in either the positive or the negative transition. $V_{IH(min)}$ for 74XX gates is +2 V; this level is not reached until 800 ns after the start of the pulse, $V_{IL(max)}$ is not reached at all. At higher clock-pulse rates any divide-by two circuit would malfunction, giving erratic output.

Any gates such as the 7473 or 74112 which had such pulses applied as clock pulses would not operate correctly, if they worked at all. The fact that $V_{IL(max)}$ is not reached at all and that $V_{IH(min)}$ is delayed until 800 ns after the start of the original pulse means that faulty clocking would occur and the circuit would malfunction. No circuit would be constructed with such values in circuit; however, under fault conditions when a gate has gone open circuit or a very badly oxidised joint as a result of bad soldering has occurred, then such conditions could apply.

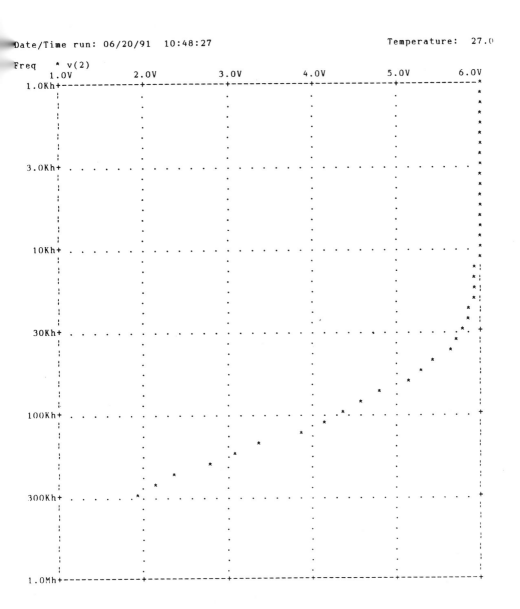

Figure 4.2.3 Swept frequency response

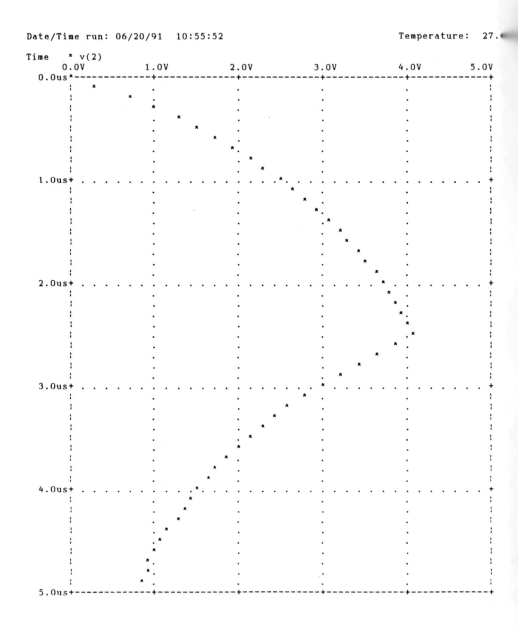

Figure 4.2.4 Transient response

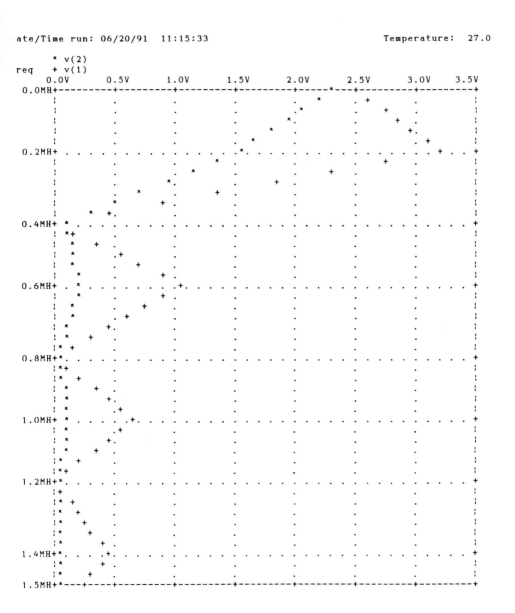

Figure 4.2.5 Fourier response analysis

The results for the Fourier analysis, figure 4.2.5, show that all components of the output pulse which affect the pulse shape have been attenuated and have also suffered large nominal and hence normalised phase shifts. The corners of the pulse have therefore been severely distorted and the losses in amplitude suffered by the fundamental and the lower-order odd harmonics (3rd and 5th) have greatly reduced the pulse's amplitude.

Q.4.3

The following are three methods of reducing the number of errors that can occur in the reception of digital systems. For each method, explain its features and design a circuit that will perform the function described:

(a) parity checking,

(b) use of a Gray code and

(c) use of a Hamming code.

A.4.3

(a) In many digital systems where a constant word length is used, an extra bit is added to the word (the parity bit) and used as a check bit.

There are two ways that the parity bit can be added: to produce *even parity* where the total number of ones in the word and the parity bit together must be an even number, or it can be added to produce *odd parity* where the total number of ones in the word and the parity bit together must be an odd number. If one bit that is transmitted is received as a 1 instead of a 0 or a 0 instead of a 1, then the parity detection circuit will detect that the parity bit does not agree with the received word. If more than two bits both change in the same way (e.g. from 0 to 1 or vice versa) then the parity bit will agree with the number of 1s or 0s received and the error will not be detected.

The system for parity checking in a data link is shown in figure 4.3.1. The transmitting circuits will check each word before it is finally transmitted, and insert the parity bit for the chosen parity. The receiver will then check each word as it is received to ensure that the received parity bit agrees with the number of bits received.

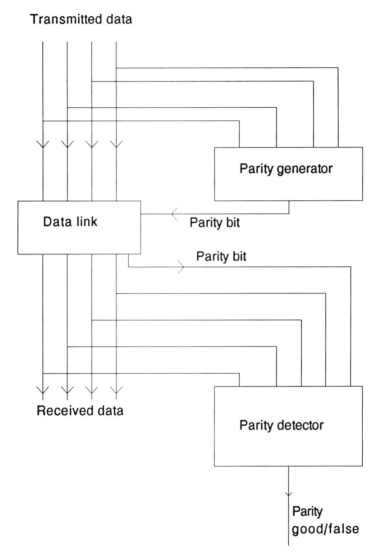

Figure 4.3.1 Basic parity checking circuit

The principle of generating an even parity bit for a 3-bit word can be seen by the truth table in figure 4.3.2, where A, B and C are the data inputs and P is the parity bit.

The Karnaugh map in figure 4.3.3 shows a pattern that resembles the black and white squares on a chessboard. The Karnaugh map cannot

A	B	C	P
0	0	0	0
1	0	0	1
0	1	0	1
0	0	1	1
1	1	0	0
1	0	1	0
0	1	1	0
1	1	1	1

Figure 4.3.2 Truth table for a 3-bit word with even parity

AB / C	00	01	11	10
0		1		1
1	1		1	

Figure 4.3.3 Karnaugh map for even parity with a 3-bit data word

be minimised; its Boolean expression reflects the Boolean form of exclusive-OR (X-OR) gates.

The truth table for a 2-input X-OR gate and its circuit diagram symbol are shown in figure 4.3.4.

The circuit diagram for the required parity bit generator is shown in figure 4.3.5.

A 3-bit parity checking receive circuit is also constructed from X-OR gates as shown in figure 4.3.6.

It is however not normal to construct either a parity bit generator or detector from individual ICs, but rather to use an MSI device to achieve

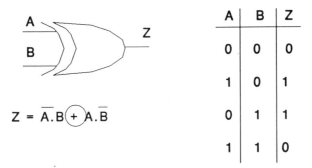

$$Z = \overline{A}.B + A.\overline{B}$$

A	B	Z
0	0	0
1	0	1
0	1	1
1	1	0

Figure 4.3.4 Circuit diagram symbol, truth table and Boolean identity for a 2-input X-OR gate

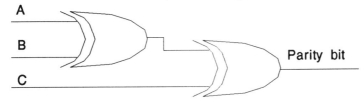

Figure 4.3.5 Parity bit generator for even parity with a 3-bit word

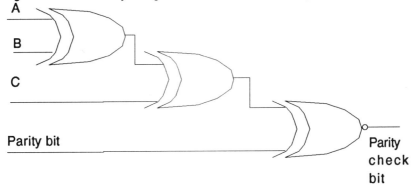

Figure 4.3.6 A parity check circuit for received 3-bit word with a parity bit added

the function. Figure 4.3.7 shows the truth table and circuit diagram symbol for an SN74180 device. It can function as either a parity generator or checker for both odd and even parity.

The truth table shows in the last two lines how the device acts as a parity checker. The first column for these lines deals with the summing of

FUNCTION TABLE

INPUTS			OUTPUTS	
Σ OF H's AT A THRU H	EVEN	ODD	Σ EVEN	Σ ODD
EVEN	H	L	H	L
ODD	H	L	L	H
EVEN	L	H	L	H
ODD	L	H	H	L
X	H	H	L	L
X	L	L	H	H

H = high level, L = low level, X = irrelevant

SN54180 ... J OR W PACKAGE
SN74180 ... J OR N PACKAGE
(TOP VIEW)

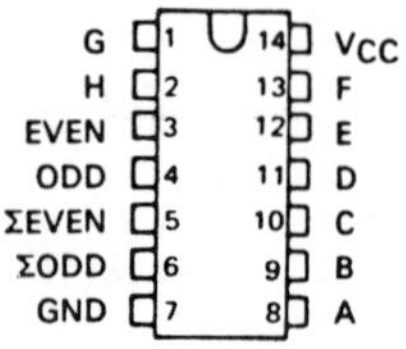

```
       G  □1  ∪ 14□  VCC
       H  □2    13□  F
    EVEN  □3    12□  E
     ODD  □4    11□  D
   ΣEVEN  □5    10□  C
    ΣODD  □6     9□  B
     GND  □7     8□  A
```

Figure 4.3.7 SN74180 9_bit parity checker generator

the 8-bit input word and shows that when the EVEN and ODD inputs are both HIGH, then both EVEN and ODD *outputs* are LOW. When these inputs are set LOW, the resulting output is HIGH.

The truth table shows in the first four lines how the IC operates as a parity bit generator; in line 1 the number of 1s input is EVEN and the EVEN input line is marked HIGH; the parity bit output on pin 5 is HIGH.

This output forms the 9th bit in the word. At the receiving end of the data system the 8 data bits would be input as bits A-H and the 9th bit to the EVEN input, while the ODD input was connected to 0 V. Line 1 then would result in the generation of a HIGH output on pin 5 if both the

switching characteristics, V_{CC} = 5 V, T_A = 25°C

PARAMETER[†]	FROM (INPUT)	TO (OUTPUT)	TEST CONDITIONS	MIN	TYP	MAX	UNIT
t_{PLH}	Data	Σ Even	C_L = 15 pF, R_L = 400 Ω, Odd input grounded, See Note 3		40	60	ns
t_{PHL}					45	68	
t_{PLH}	Data	Σ Odd			32	48	ns
t_{PHL}					25	38	
t_{PLH}	Data	Σ Even	C_L = 15 pF, R_L = 400 Ω, Even input grounded, See Note 3		32	48	ns
t_{PHL}					25	38	
t_{PLH}	Data	Σ Odd			40	60	ns
t_{PHL}					45	68	
t_{PLH}	Even or Odd	Σ Even or Σ Odd	C_L = 15 pF, R_L = 400 Ω, See Note 3		13	20	ns
t_{PHL}					7	10	

Figure 4.3.8 Switching characteristics for an SN74180

number of bits received is *even* and the EVEN input is HIGH. If however the EVEN input is HIGH but the number of bits received is ODD, then pin 5 is LOW to indicate that parity is wrong for that word.

Lines 3-4 show how ODD parity is checked in the same way.

Figure 4.3.8 shows the switching characteristics of the device.

(b) When a binary number such as 101111 has another 1 added, the addition gives the result 110000. Of the six bits, five change their value. It is possible that an error could occur in the addition of the bits as so many binary bits are changing at the same time.

The Gray code unlike binary is an *unweighted* code, so the positions of the bits in the code do not have a weight attached to them; because of this they cannot be used in arithmetic operations but are used

Decimal	Binary code	Gray code
0	0000	0000
1	0001	0001
2	0010	0011
3	0011	0010
4	0100	0110
5	0101	0111
6	0110	0101
7	0111	0100
8	1000	1100
9	1001	1101
10	1010	1111

Figure 4.3.9 Decimal numbers and their binary and Gray codes

in some types of A-D converters and in input/output devices such as optical shaft encoders.

Figure 4.3.9 shows that only one bit changes at a time in the Gray code, and that the first bit in the Gray code is the same as the first bit in binary. The second bit in the Gray code is formed by the exclusive-OR of the first and second bits of the binary number. The third bit in the Gray code is formed from the exclusive-OR of the second and third bits in the binary number. Each successive bit in the Gray code is formed in a similar way.

Figure 4.3.10 shows a circuit that could generate Gray code from a binary input.

Converting from Gray code to binary will leave the first bit unchanged. If the second bit in the Gray code is a 0, the second binary

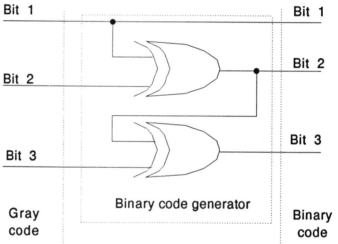

Figure 4.3.10 System diagram for the generation of binary code from Gray code

bit will be the same as the first; if it is a 1 then the second binary bit is the inverse of the first bit. This is repeated for all the bits.

Figure 4.3.11 shows a circuit that would generate binary output from Gray code input.

(c) While the parity bit can indicate that an error has occurred in a received word when either 1 or 3 bits are incorrect, it can do no more than that. A Hamming code can both detect and correct errors in a received word. It uses a series of three parity check bits each of which checks for even parity. They are each arranged to check 3 of the four data bits.

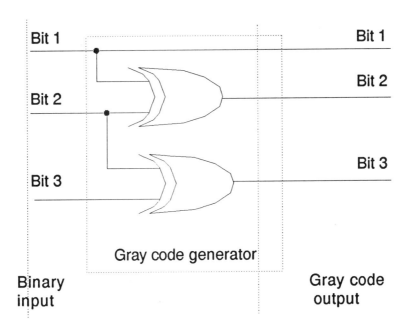

Figure 4.3.11 System diagram for a Gray code generator

A 4-bit data word is to be transmitted using a Hamming code for a single error; assume the word to be transmitted is 1001. Then the coded word that is transmitted is as shown in figure 4.3.12; the bits checked by each parity bit are also shown.

D4	D3	D2	P3	D1	P2	P1
X		X		X		X
X		X		X	X	
X	X	X	X			

Data words: D4, D3, D2 and D1.
Parity bits: P3, P2 and P1.

Figure 4.3.12 Data word and parity bits in Hamming code

The transmitted word is 1001, so that D4 = 1, D3 = 0, D5 = 0 and D1 = 1; so the parity bits that are generated and put into the coded word are:

P1 checks D4, D2 and D1; these give even parity and so P1 = 0.

P2 checks D4, D3 and D1; these give even parity and so P2 = 0.

P3 checks D4, D3 and D2; these do not give even parity and hence P3 = 1.

So the coded word for transmission is 1001100.

A circuit for generating one of the parity check digits is shown in figure 4.3.13.

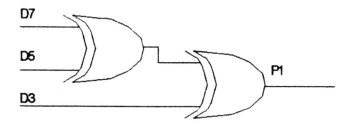

Figure 4.3.13 Hamming code parity bit generator for bits D7,D5 and D3

If the received word is 1100100, then clearly D3 has been incorrectly received. Now D4 = 1, D3 = 1, D2 = 0 and D1 = 1. The checking of the parity bits with the received word would show:

As D4 = 1, D2 = 0 and D1 = 1, P1 is 0; which is correct.

As D4 = 1, D3 = 1 and D1 = 1, P2 is now 1; which is incorrect.

As D4 = 1, D3 = 1 and D2 = 0, P3 is now 0; which is also incorrect.

As both P3 and P2 fail, the error must be a bit which is common to both parity bits. D4 must be correct as it is also checked by P1 and that

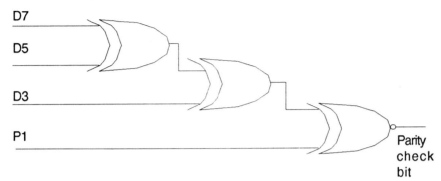

Figure 4.3.14 A parity check circuit for received Hamming code

check was correct. Hence as the only other common bit is D3; this is wrong.

5 Signal Processing

Prior Knowledge

You should be familiar with the following topics :

(a) The principles of analogue-to-digital and digital-to-analogue conversion.

(b) A method of converting analogue signals to digital signals, and a method of converting digital signals to analogue signals.

A review question on these topics occurs in **Q.1.6**.

Q.5.1

(a) What is an analogue-to-digital converter?

(b) The analogue signal below is to be converted into a digital signal. Explain how the following could affect the conversion process:

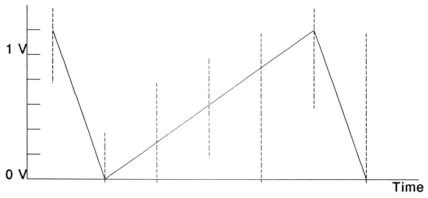

(1) The signals bandwidth,

(2) the sampling rate used,

(3) the resolution and

(4) the linearity of the converter.

138

A.5.1

(a) Analogue-to-digital conversion is the process of converting an analogue input signal into a corresponding digital signal.

(b) The process of conversion consists of taking a sample of the analogue signal and converting it into the corresponding digital code.

A-D converters have as output a finite number of digital bits; this is often 4, 8, 10, 12 or more. An analogue signal must be processed during conversion so that all its characteristics are contained in the digital word that represents it. The analogue signal can have any value of amplitude at any time, but these values must be converted by the A-D converter into the number of bits that are available within the chosen system. If the A-D converter is being used with an 8-bit microprocessor system then, it is likely that an 8-bit A-D converter will be used.

Figure 5.1.1 shows how at discrete time intervals the analogue input signal is **sampled** by the A-D converter. It is these samples taken at regular time intervals that are converted into digital code. For an 8-bit A-D

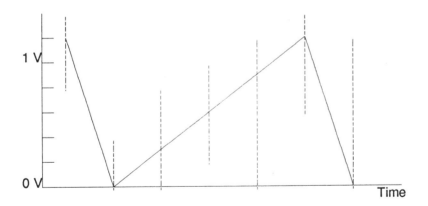

Figure 5.1.1 Sampling periods for A-D conversion

converter there are 256 unique combinations of bits that can be used to contain the characteristics of the input signal. The more samples that are taken, the more faithfully will the characteristics of the input signal be retained, particularly when it is changing rapidly.

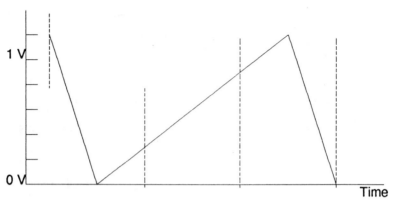

Figure 5.1.2 Sampling at half the rate of figure 5.1.1

In figure 5.1.2 the rate at which the samples are taken has been halved from that in figure 5.1.1; the result is that during the signal's positive to negative transition no sample was taken. If the rate of sampling were made very low and samples were only taken at points A and B, then the A-D converter would assume (correctly in this case !) that there was no signal present and produce the code for 0 V, ignoring the fact that the signal has finite values between these time intervals (this phenomenon is known as **aliasing**). It can be shown by the Sampling theorem that the **minimum rate** at which a signal must be sampled to retain its characteristics is **at twice the highest frequency** that is contained in the analogue signal. The higher the bandwidth of the input signal, the higher must be the sampling rate.

It is the analogue input signal that establishes this criterion; the A-D converter must accommodate the requirement as well as it is able.

The amplitude levels in figure 5.1.2 will then have to be converted into digital code. With 256 possible codes for an 8-bit converter a unique code will have to be generated for this amplitude level. Figure 5.1.3 shows the first two amplitude samples from the input being compared with the digital codes representing the voltage level at which they occur. At X the amplitude corresponds exactly to the code 01110011, and so the A-D converter will take this word as being the correct code.

At Y the sampled amplitude level corresponds exactly neither to 01110001 nor to 01110000; it falls nearer to the latter value than the first,

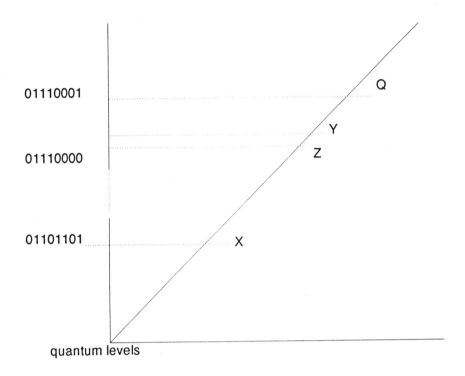

Figure 5.1.3 Quantisation levels and errors

and so this word is taken as the digital code for this level. It is however **incorrect,** as 01110000 represents the voltage level present at point Z on the waveform. This error is know as **a quantisation error** and cannot be totally eliminated. It can however be reduced, and the greater the number of bits that are used the closer together are the quantisation levels and hence the lower the absolute error that can occur between each of the levels. If the signal is converted back to analogue form from the digital signal, then 01110000 will be converted to the voltage level at Z and not that at Y. The reduction in the error or noise produced by the increase in the number of bits can be shown to be 6 dB for each extra bit used.

The difference in the values of analogue signal level between points Y and Q represents a change of only one quantum level and hence of one binary bit in the digital signal. This change of one LSB represents the minimum change in the amplitude of the analogue signal that can be accommodated by the A-D converter. It is called the **resolution** of the converter. It must not be forgotten that while the sample being converted is a voltage level sample, the transducer that produced this voltage could well have been measuring temperature or the rotational speed of a shaft and that the A-D converter's resolution affects the minimum change in these quantities that can be resolved in the conversion.

During the entire process of A-D conversion it is assumed that the conversion process is linear. Figure 5.1.4 shows the ideal characteristic between the minimum and maximum analogue levels and their corresponding minimum and maximum digital codes. Any non-linearity will produce a non-ideal characteristic and will entail producing a "best fit" line for the converter. It is assumed that with an analogue input voltage of 0 V, the digital output code will be zero. Any dc signal that is present will result in a shift in level so that there is no zero digital output code but one that is **offset** by an amount corresponding to the value of the dc component. There is a relationship between the A-D converter's

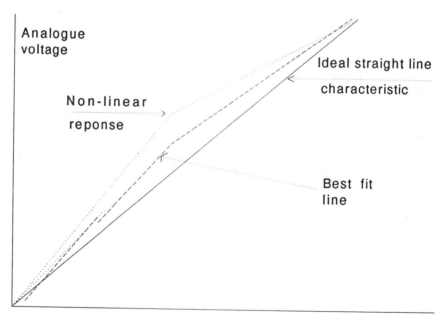

Figure 5.1.4 Non-linearity in an A-D converter

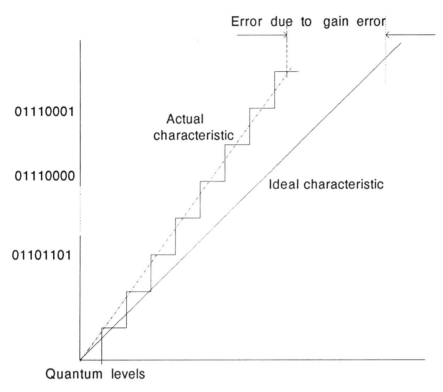

Figure 5.1.5   A-D converter showing a gain error

analogue values and the digital code values. There can be a **gain error** which is the amount by which the actual scale values are different from the designed values. This gain error will determine the slope of the A-D converter's transfer characteristic. The broken line in figure 5.1.5 shows the gain error for a converter that has a slope that differs from the ideal. Gain errors can be taken into account during the calibration of the A-D converter.

Q.5.2

(1) Explain what an **R-2R** ladder network is and how it can be used to provide D-A conversion. What errors could occur in a D-A converter using such a network?

(2) Explain how the ZN426E device shown below can be connected to be used as a D-A converter.

A.5.2

(1) An **R-2R** ladder network is shown in figure 5.2.1. The resistors have values such that the 2R resistor has twice the resistance of the **R** resistor. The 2R resistors are connected by an electronic switch either to 0 V or to an externally applied reference voltage. The electronic switches are connected to the reference voltage by a 1; a 0 switches them to 0 V. If all the inputs are a 0 then clearly the output is 0 V. If (as in figure 5.2.2(a)) they are all at 1 then the output voltage is the reference voltage; if the input bits are 110, then (as shown in figure 5.2.2.(b)) the output voltage is three-quarters of the reference voltage.

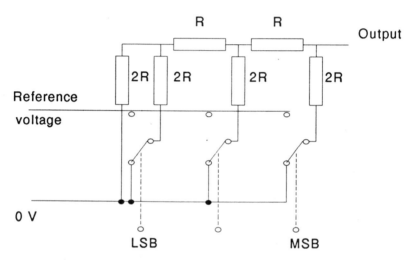

Figure 5.2.1 R-2R ladder network

This type of circuit uses only two values of resistors and it is their ratio rather than their exact value which is important. The number of resistors in the ladder can be extended to accommodate as many bits as necessary.

Errors could occur if either the resistors are not perfectly matched or the switches have a finite value of resistance. We assume that when the input to the converter is increased by 1 LSB then the output will increase in a staircase manner as shown in figure 5.2.3(a); such increases are called **monotonic** increases. A non-monotonic converter would cause the output to decrease instead of increase as shown in

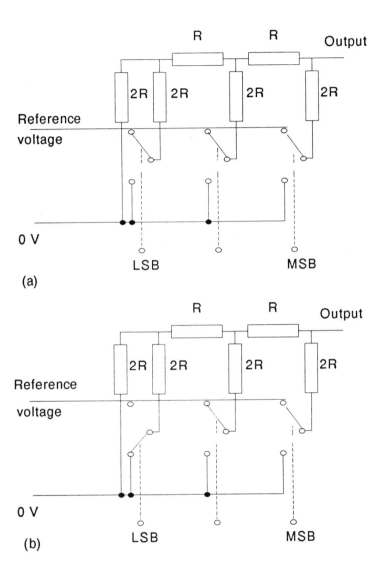

Figure 5.2.2 R-2R ladder network

(a) with connections to reference voltage,

(b) with bits set at 110

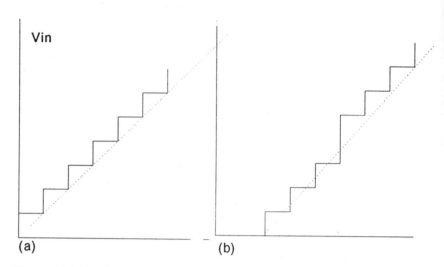

Figure 5.2.3   Monotonicity in converter transfer characteristics

(a) a monotonic converter

(b) a non-monotonic converter, with the same linear rise in input.

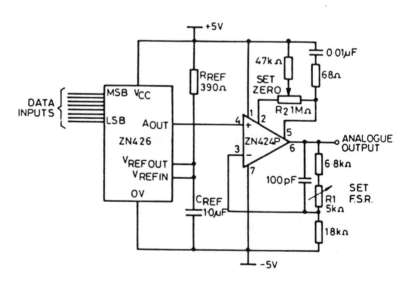

Figure 5.2.4 ZN 426E used an a D-A converter

figure 5.2.3(b). Linearity errors in a monotonic converter are usually in the range ±0.5 LSB; this is the amount by which a point on the converter's transfer characteristic varies from the line connecting 0 V to the reference voltage.

The resolution of the converter can also cause errors. Resolution is **not** related to linearity, it is a function of the number of bits used; it represents the smallest analogue change that will occur at the output following a change of 1 LSB in the digital input. There is a finite time for a change at the input to allow the input to settle to its final value; the figure given is usually a typical value and errors would occur in the analogue output waveform if the output were not allowed to settle to its final value.

(2) The circuit given in the question is of a ZN426E 8-bit D-A converter. It is compatible with both TTL and 5 V CMOS and operates from a 5 V supply connected to pin 14, with pin 7 at 0 V. The analogue output is from pin 4 and the digital inputs are on pins 1- 8; with pin 1 being the MSB and pin 8 the LSB. Figure 5.2.4 shows the connections needed to provide an analogue output. Pins 6 and 5 are connected together and taken to V_{CC} via a small-value resistor, which is decoupled by a capacitor. The analogue amplifier connected to pin 4 removes any offset voltage that may be present at the D-A converter's output, and also calibrates the converter by allowing the gain of the op-amp to be altered with **R1**.

Q.5.3

The ZN435 is described as being able to operate as both a "ramp and compare ADC" and as a "tracking ADC". Explain these terms and show how the device can perform these functions.

A.5.3

A "ramp and compare ADC" contains a counter; at the start of the conversion the counter is reset to zero. Clock pulses are applied to the counter and counted. The logic levels representing the value of the count are applied to the inputs of a D-A converter so that as the count increases so does the amplitude of the analogue signal being produced. When the amplitude of the external analogue signal is equal to the amplitude of the output of the D-A converter the count is stopped and the value held in the counter represents the digital equivalent of the amplitude of the analogue input signal. Figure 5.3.1 shows the basic arrangement for a ramp and compare converter. The time taken for such a converter to complete its conversion is not fixed but will depend on the input clock frequency and the amplitude of the external analogue signal.

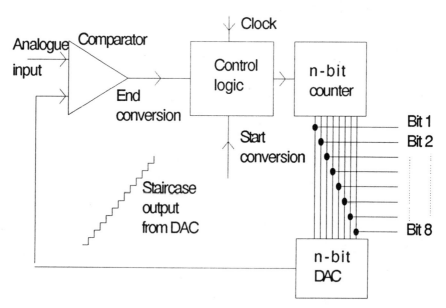

Figure 5.3.1 Ramp and compare ADC, circuit diagram

For this device, the maximum quoted clock frequency is 500 kHz; with this clock rate the time to count the maximum possible number of 256 clock pulses would be:

256 x 2 = 512 microseconds.

To this must also be added additional fixed propagation delays as signals pass through the logic circuits.

A "tracking ADC" is similar to the ramp and compare ADC; however in this latter type the counter is reset to zero and when conversion starts it counts upwards. The tracking converter has an up-down counter and the comparator controls the direction of the count; again as the count progresses a D-A converter produces an analogue output which is proportional to the digital value held in the counter. Figure 5.3.2 shows how a comparator is connected to control the direction of the count. If the output from the D-A converter is **less** than the analogue input, then the comparator will give an output which will cause the counter to count up. This will increase the amplitude of the analogue output from the D-A converter until it exceeds the amplitude of the external analogue signal. The output of the comparator changes and a down count begins; the down count is only for 1 LSB. This causes the control to change to **up**. The process continues with changes of ±1 LSB

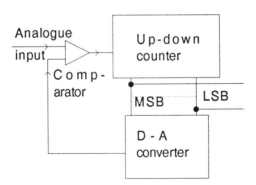

Figure 5.3.2 Tracking A-D converter

occurring around the correct value. Small changes in amplitude of the external analogue signal are quickly followed and the conversion time can be small.

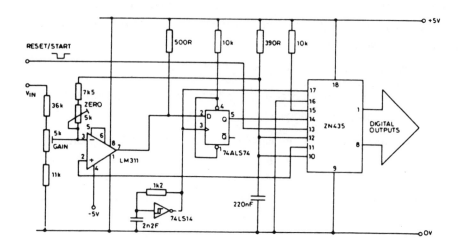

Figure 5.3.3 ZN435 as a ramp and compare converter

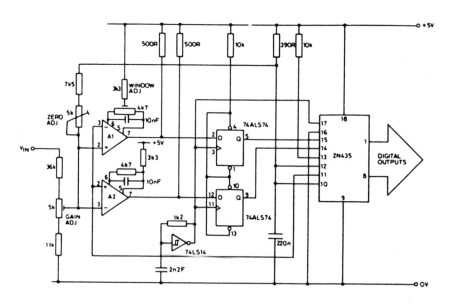

Figure 5.3.4 ZN435 as a tracking converter

The use of the ZN435 as a ramp and compare converter is shown in figure 5.3.3. and as a tracking converter in figure 5.3.4.

Q.5.4

Explain, using a block diagram the main components of a single channel data acquisition system using an analogue preamplifier, a sample-and-hold circuit and a successive-approximation converter. Outline the function of each block of the system.

A.5.4.

The block diagram of the system is shown in figure 5.4.1.

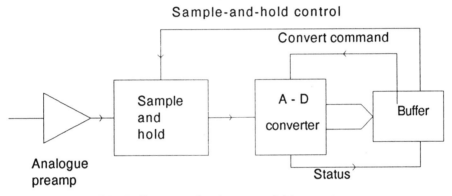

Figure 5.4.1 Block diagram of a data acquisition system

The pre-amp may fill one of many functions in the system. It could be used:

(1) As an impedance buffer, to match the sample-and-hold's impedance to that of the transducer that feeds it.

(2) As an amplifier to increase the level of the incoming signal so that it matches the voltage range of the A-D converter better.

(3) As an active attenuator when the amplitude of the transducer's output signal is too large.

(4) To remove common-mode signals that may have been introduced during the transmission of the signal. These signals are often a result of differing earth potentials between the transmitting and receiving points or are induced into the transmission system externally.

They should be considered as noise, and steps be taken to remove them.

(5) To introduce a mathematical function such as a logarithmic function for some special purpose.

(6) To provide a combination of the functions (1) - (5) above, to give the best results from the A - D conversion process.

The sample-and-hold circuit is used as an acquisition device to acquire the analogue signal before conversion begins, and then to keep it while the conversion process is carried out. The ideal model of a sample-and-hold circuit is that of a capacitor that is connected to a switch; the switch is usually in such a position that it is connected to the analogue input signal (position A in figure 5.4.2). In this position, the capacitor is at

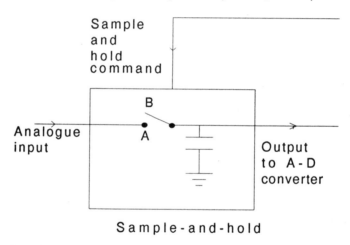

Sample-and-hold

Figure 5.4.2   Sample-and-hold system

the same amplitude level as the input signal. When the switch is open (and assuming a perfect capacitor) the voltage across the capacitor is held constant at the instantaneous value that was present when the switch was closed. This value is constant during the time that the A-D conversion takes place; for each of the samples that the sample and hold contains, the converter will produce a digitally coded signal.

A successive approximation converter basically consists of an up-down counter which works under the control of a logic programmer, a D-A converter and a comparator.

The programmer sets the most significant bit of the counter to 1 and the output of the D-A converter is compared with the amplitude of the analogue signal. Three possible results can occur as a result of this comparison:

(1) The amplitudes are the same, at which happy result the count is stopped and the value in the counter is the correct digitally coded value.

(2) The amplitude of the analogue signal is **greater** than that from the D-A converter; the programmer then applies the next most significant bit to the D-A converter and compares again.

(3) The amplitude of the analogue signal is **smaller** than the D-A's output; the programmer then applies the next most significant bit to the D-A converter and compares again.

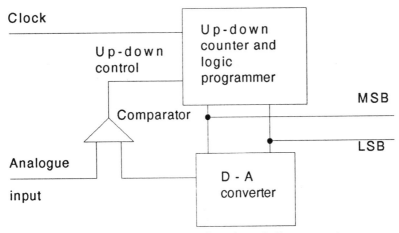

Figure 5.4.3 Successive approximation A-D converter

When the results of (2) and (3) eventually produce a value in the counter which after comparison with the input signal is the same then the count is stopped and conversion is complete.

In an 8-bit system the total conversion time is a maximum of 8-clock pulse periods as opposed to 256 for a ramp and compare converter.

Q.5.5

(a) Explain how multiplexing of channels can enable a converter to deal with more than one input signal.

(b) Use the diagram below to explain how the ZN437 can be used in a data acquisition system.

A.5.5

(a) Multiplexing is the process of enabling more that one signal to use a transmission path or a circuit. It can be accomplished in one of two ways, either by **Time Division Multiplexing** (TDM) or by **Frequency Division Multiplexing** (FDM), and both these methods are shown in figure 5.5.1.

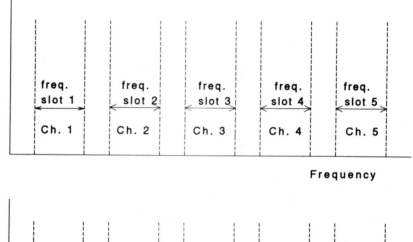

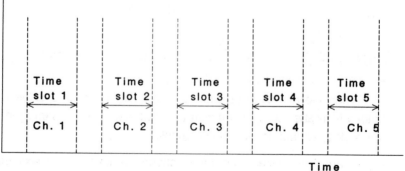

Figure 5.5.1   FDM and TDM

Frequency division multiplexing is accomplished by using a frequency translation process, so that each channel is given a unique frequency allocation within the system's bandwidth; it is more frequently used for communications systems than for A-D-A conversion.

Time division multiplexing allocates each of the system's channels a time slot during which the selected channel has exclusive use of the system. It can be represented as a pair of rotary switches, one at the transmitting and one at the receiving terminal. The two switches are synchronised so that they are both connected to the same channel's input and output at the same time. Figure 5.5.2 shows a TDM transmission system for a four-channel system.

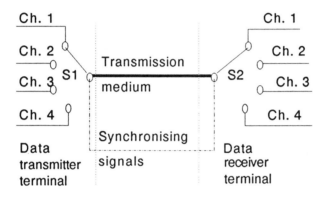

Figure 5.5.2 Four-channel TDM system

There are several methods in which multiplexing can be accomplished in an A-D converter.

(1) By giving each channel its own A-D system and multiplexing the digital outputs. This would require, for an 8-bit system, 8 complete A-D systems, each totally complete. This would add to the system's complexity and cost.

(b) Figure 5.5.3 shows a multiplexing system that has a common sample and hold and converter for each channel; the multiplexing occurs prior to this so that the conversion process is shared between the input signals, each being allocated a unique time slot. The results of the conversion are then stored in a register until they are required. When a

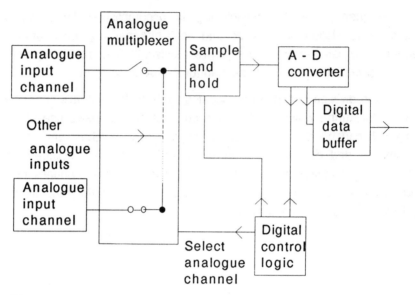

Figure 5.5.3   Multi-channel data acquisition system

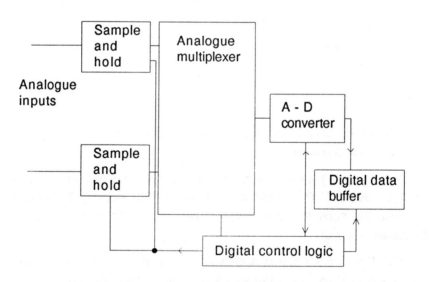

Figure 5.5.4 Multi-channel data acquisition system with
              simultaneous sampling of the input channels

DB7	DB6	DB5	DB4	DB3	DB2	DB1	DB0
START	CLOCK PRE-DIVIDER		$\overline{CY}$	$\overline{SQ}$	ANALOGUE INPUT		
1	X	X	1	1	X	X	X

(a) Initialisation word

DB7	DB6	DB5	DB4	DB3	DB2	DB1	DB0
START	CLOCK PRE-DIVIDER		$\overline{CY}$	$\overline{SQ}$	ANALOGUE INPUT		
0	X	X	1	1	X	X	X

(b) Control word for a single conversion of a named channel

DB7	DB6	DB5	DB4	DB3	DB2	DB1	DB0
START	CLOCK PRE-DIVIDER		$\overline{CY}$	$\overline{SQ}$	ANALOGUE INPUT		
0	X	X	0	1	X	X	X

(c) Control word to commence a continuous conversion of a specified analogue input

DB7	DB6	DB5	DB4	DB3	DB2	DB1	DB0
START	CLOCK PRE-DIVIDER		$\overline{CY}$	$\overline{SQ}$	ANALOGUE INPUT		
1	X	X	1	1	X	X	X

(d) Control word to stop a continuous conversion of a specified analogue channel

Figure 5.5.5 Format of control signals

conversion is complete, the next channel is selected and has sole use of the converter.

(c) Figure 5.5.4 shows an alternative arrangement for multiplexing; here the analogue channels each have their own sample-and-hold circuits and multiplexing occurs after this. This arrangement allows the sample-and-holds all to be switched at the same time, so that the state of the variables being acquired is obtained at the same instant of time. The conversion takes place after the sample-and-holds have acquired the data. The next samples are acquired after all the channels have been converted.

(d) The figure in the question shows the analogue multiplexer receiving the analogue inputs, hence system (3) would be used here, with each channel having its own sample-and-hold circuitry. These would of course, be controlled by the same microprocessor that controls the rest of the conversion process, so there are no timing errors. The IC can be programmed by the input of control words to work in any of four ways dependent on the overall system's requirements:

(1) A single conversion from a specified channel.

(2) A continuous conversion from a specified channel.

(3) A single conversion on all eight channels.

(4) A continuous conversion on all eight channels.

To commence conversion, an "initialisation word" must be sent; further operations are controlled by selecting which of the modes (1)-(4) is required by applying the correct signals to the pins controlling SEQUENCE (SQ), CYCLING (CY) and the START. The outline form of these signals is shown in figure 5.5.5. (**Note complete descriptions** of the action of these signals are not given.)

The overall control of the A-D conversion, the selection of conversion modes, the reading of the digital data and the selection of input channel are externally controlled by a microprocessor based system. (The data sheet gives applications using 8086/8 and Z80 microprocessors.)

Q.5.6

(1) Explain how propagation delays and noise margins could cause problems when interconnecting different logic families.

(2) Explain why and how the following logic families require interfacing devices:

(a) TTL to CMOS,

(b) TTL to ECL.

A.5.6

(1) An ECL gate can work at a clock rate 200 MHz, a standard TTL device has a maximum of 35 MHz. The maximum speed at which a combination of the two devices could work at is that of the slower, i.e. 35 MHz. There are applications where the speed of the various logic families could be used to their fullest extent. A VHF frequency counter, could for example, have its counter constructed using ECL devices, with slower-speed TTL or CMOS being used for the arithmetic and general-purpose logic where there is no advantage in using more costly, very high-speed devices.

The worst state noise margins that exist for a logic family can be taken as:

LOW noise margin = V_{IL} - V_{OL} and

HIGH noise margin = V_{OH} - V_{IH}

Figure 5.6.1 shows the noise margins for the TTL, CMOS and ECL families.

Any signal that causes a gate's input level to either rise or fall below these worst-case levels can cause faulty operation. If a LOW state for a TTL device is forced by a noise transient above 0.4 V then the device moves into the area which is not normally used; this is shown in figure 5.6.2. For CMOS this value would be 1.65 V for a LOW input state.

(2a)

There are two possible solutions, dependent upon whether the CMOS is connected to a common 5 V rail with the TTL or whether it uses

Logic family	$V_{IL} - V_{OL}$ = LOW Noise margin	$V_{OH} - V_{IH}$ = HIGH Noise margin
TTL	0.8 - 0.4 = 0.4 V	2.4 - 0.4 = 0.V
CMOS V_{CC} = 5 V	1.66 - 0.01= 1.65 V	4.99 -3.33=1.66 V
ECL V_{CC} = -5.2 V	1.475-1.63=-.015 V	0.98 - 1.105=-.0125 V

Figure 5.6.1 Noise immunity for various logic famlies

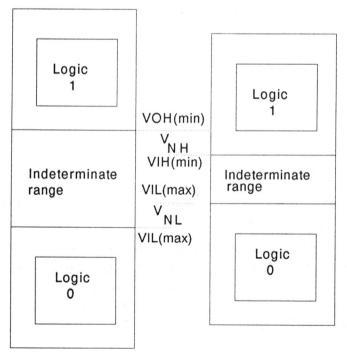

Figure 5.6.2   TTL noise margins

a separate supply. There are no fan out problems as the impedance of CMOS is negligible compared with TTL.

When both families share a common supply it is possible to drive CMOS directly from TTL. The normal method of doing this is shown in figure 5.6.3 where a "pull up" resistor is connected to the 5 V rail between the TTL output and the CMOS input. This causes the TTL's HIGH voltage to rise to 5 V so that the CMOS is driven with no loss of noise immunity.

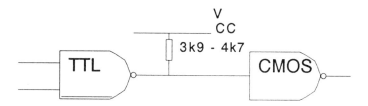

Figure 5.6.3 TTL to CMOS interconnections with a common
              power supply

When the CMOS device is running at a higher voltage, the level of the TTL cannot be so easily altered. The easiest solution is to use an open collector TTL device such as a 7406, connected as shown in figure 5.6.4.

To drive TTL from CMOS requires the provision of a sufficiently large sink current when the TTL is LOW. If the devices are both connected to 5 V then a CMOS gate can drive one 74LS input. The

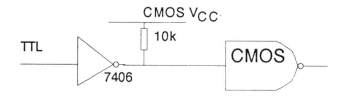

Figure 5.6.4 TTL to CMOS interconnections with separate
              power supplies

CMOS family of devices includes the 4009 and 4010 buffers; both these have a sink current of 6 mA when they are LOW, and so could be used to drive up to three standard TTL gates. They are constructed with separate power supply connections for their input and output stages, so that they can be used when CMOS and TTL have different power supplies. Such an arrangement is shown in figure 5.6.5.

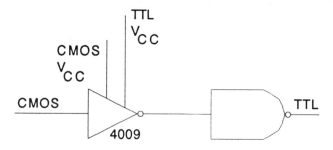

Figure 5.6.5 CMOS to TTL using a 4009 inverting buffer

(2b)

TTL to ECL again can be considered for two cases, depending on whether they share common 5 V supplies or the TTL device is at 5 V and the ECL at -5.2 V.

	TTL output	ECL input
High level output	V_{OH} = 2.4 min	V_{IH} = 3.895 min
	I_{OH} = 400 uA max	I_{IH} = 250 uA
Low level output	V_{OL} = 0.4 V max	V_{IH} = 3.5 V max
	I_{OL} = 16 mA	I_{IH} = 0.5 uA

Figure 5.6.6 Comparison of TTL and ECL voltage and current levels

Figure 5.6.6 shows the relationship between the HIGH and LOW voltage levels for both families. There is clearly no possibility of direct connection, and so level shifting must be used.

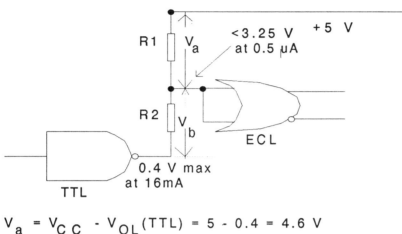

$$V_a = V_{CC} - V_{OL}(TTL) = 5 - 0.4 = 4.6 \text{ V}$$

$$V_b = V_{ILb}(ECL) - V_{OL}(TTL) = 3.5 - 0.4 = 3.1 \text{ V}$$

$$V_c = V_a - V_b = 4.6 - 3.1 = 1.5 \text{ V}$$

Figure 5.6.7   Low level logic voltages and currents for ECL and TTL interfacing

Figure 5.6.7 shows one possible method of level changing; the currents and voltage shown are for the LOW state for both gates. A TTL gate will sink 16 mA to guarantee a maximum value of V_{OL} of 0.4 V; a value of 10 mA can be assumed. The current through R1 and R2 is then 10 mA.

Figure 5.6.8 shows the conditions present when the TTL's output is HIGH. As the current into the ECL gate is negligible, it can be assumed that there is no voltage drop across R1 and that the ECL's input voltage is 5 V.

When the ECL operates from -5.2 V it is usual to use a translator device such as the MC10124 which provides the correct input and output levels with no additional circuitry being required. Figure 5.6.9 shows the arrangement for one of the MC10124's four gates.

In the HIGH state the difference between the OR and the NOR output voltages of 0.65 V is enough to turn a transistor ON. In figure 5.6.10 a small npn transistor has been placed between the ECL and the TTL gates.

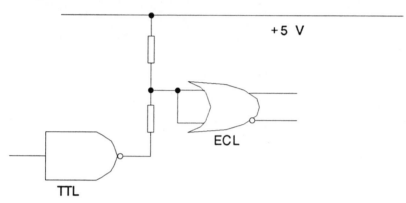

Figure 5.6.8 TTL to ECL interfacing

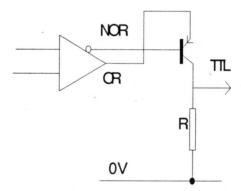

Figure 5.6.9 MC 10124 TTL-ECL translator

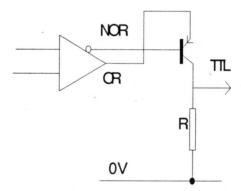

Figure 5.6.10 EC1-TTL interconnection with common +5 V supplies

When OR is HIGH, NOR is LOW so that T1 is turned ON; this pulls the input to a voltage which is seen by the TTL as a HIGH. The voltage is: $V_{OH} - V_{ce(sat)} = 4.02 - 0.2 = 3.82$ V.

It is above the 2.0 V minimum required for a TTL HIGH input.

The value for R can be found from the worst-case output current, from this the minimum value for R can be found. The maximum value for R can be found from the LOW level input conditions.

The minimum and maximum values of R are then:

$R(min) = (V_{OH} - V_{ce(sat)} / I_{OH} = 3.82/50 = 76R$.

$R(max) = V_{IL}/I_{IL} = 0.8/0.0016 = 500R$.

Choosing too low a value will cause too large a current drain on the PSU; too high a value must allow for the tolerance of the resistors used. A value of 270-330R would be acceptable.

6 Designing Systems

6.1 Introduction

The topics of design, documentation and the use of manufacturer's literature have featured many times. Nowhere are they more important than when tackling a system design. In any system the individual parts are inter-related and so a failure in one part can well cause a failure of the whole system. It follows from this that there is no part of a system that is either more or less important than any other part. This is not to say that some parts are not more difficult or more time consuming to design than others, but simply that no part of the system should be treated as "unimportant". There are no unimportant components in a system.

Equally important is the fact that while the total system may well be unique in what it is going to achieve, the individual parts of the system will almost certainly have been used by either yourself or someone else in another design. To "reinvent the wheel" is tedious, time-consuming and pointless.

It is therefore important to know what is available as system components, not only in the form of Rs, Cs and ICs, but also as *proven* designs by other competent designers. Once again manufacturers are there to help; as well as data books, they also publish application and circuit literature. These are a gold-mine of circuits that are designed by the manufacturer and often transferable to another design with no or the minimum of alteration. It is very unlikely that you will require a counter, be it synchronous, up-down, BCD, 2421 or whatever, that does not appear in literature somewhere. You can also have the confidence that the success rate from implementing these circuit designs is very high indeed.

As well as manufacturer's literature there are also available many books that feature only circuits; these usually give some ideas as to the applications that they are suitable for, and often how the design may be altered for another application.

If you are working with only CMOS, TTL or ECL, then provided the circuits that you are interconnecting are inter-series, there should be no major problems. If for example CMOS and ECL are mixed for an application, provided the interfacing is correct for both voltage level and speed of operation, then again no real problems should occur.

There are also "freebies" in the form of magazines which are supplied free by many firms as a form of advertising, and these contain many interesting design ideas. The designs here, though, often do not always contain the detail that is present in manufacturer's literature.

Accepting that someone, somewhere, has possibly designed a circuit broadly on the lines of the one that you are going to work on, then it is relevant to engage in one of the most important parts of designing; asking questions of other people and listening to their answers. This "bouncing ideas around" is vital. Accept the fact that how ever dear to your own heart a project may be, there will exist someone who has at the very least worked on something parallel or knows a source of information that is relevant. It makes sense to plug into these ideas and use or modify them where they are relevant, or discard them if they do not fit.

A time honoured maxim may be misquoted as:

Design a bit, simulate a bit, built a bit, test a bit, and document all the time.

6.2 Designing Systems

The design of a system requires a technique that is sound and has a basis in engineering and science. Such a technique is Systems Analysis. The more you use this technique, the more you realise how vital it is for any design that requires more than 2-3 hour's work. (Indeed, you will find that, having once adopted it, you will use it unconsciously for most designs.)

The basis of systems analysis is to:

(1) Focus attention on the objectives of the system, by writing them down (this will normally be the technical specification).

(2) Generate alternative solutions.

(3) Suggest methods of evaluating the alternatives.

(4) Suggest methods of "looking ahead", and attempt to find the answer to "what if...?" questions.

(5) Look at ways of reaching the decision as to which is the best solution to achieve the system's objectives.

There are six basic steps in systems analysis which are represented in figure 6.1.

The technical specification

The technical specification is really a set of **objectives** that have to be attained. These will help to formulate an action plan that will implement the design. As the ultimate product of a design is required by either an individual or a group of people, then writing down what the

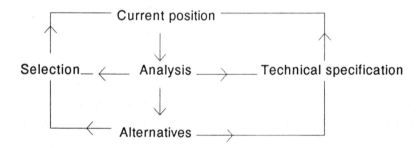

Figure 6.1 A methodology for system design

system is to do and how it is to do it is an essential task before any design can begin.

Generation of alternative solutions

We normally rely on our past experience, and the experiences of others which we can share for most of our decisions. Hence we do not normally attempt to generate solutions indefinitely, rather we tend to focus our attention on those areas which have been shown in the past to be successful. It is pointless and time consuming to consider every possible alternative solution that could exist. We would not, for example, begin to consider solutions based on thermionic valve technology; better, cheaper and more reliable technologies exist. Rather, accepting that we will use ICs, we would focus attention on solutions based more on whether we should use MOS, ECL or TTL technologies, and whether we use LSI, MSI, SSI or a customised ASIC.

The alternatives that we should focus on will often be quite global, in that we tend to treat solutions which are broadly similar to others as an inclusive group. As time costs money, and there is never enough of either, there is no point in generating alternatives forever; a point comes where the time spent can be equated with the rewards expected, and to proceed further is neither productive nor economic. This point, however, is one which only experience can show we have reached.

Evaluating the alternative solutions

The questions to be answered here can be posed as: "What are the time and monetary effects of choosing a solution?" and "What benefits and drawbacks arise from that choice?"

Suppose the choice lies between a customised IC and the use of standard "of-the-shelf" devices. How can one evaluate the decision? It is often assumed that "newest is best", and thus a customised IC answers all problems. Consider, however, the lead-in time and cost for such a device. We would need to know when some evaluation devices would be available and at what cost, as well as the expected production run so that we could evaluate the unit cost of such a decision. The use of MSI would mean a larger sized PCB and also more inter-IC wiring. Is it better to accept this or not? What is the cost of choosing this solution in both time and money? It is to be regretted that seldom are such decisions evaluated unless one is forced to do so; **there is often** more personal kudos to be gained from a solution based on "state of the art", than from a more traditional approach. The customised IC is of greatest use where a large production run is envisaged, where space would be at a premium (consider what the PCB would look like if an 80386 or 68000 were constructed in MSI rather than in VLSI technology!), or where assembly and/or production and testing would be unwieldy.

Selecting the best alternative solution

If the previous steps have been taken with care then there is often one solution that stands alone, and is the chosen answer. Where there is more than one solution, then the alternatives must be weighed carefully against the technical specification, and often with closer reference to points such as size, cost and reliability, as the technical features will certainly be present in both alternatives. If all the technical features have been highlighted and allowed for, then there is always a "best solution".

Looking ahead

It is important not simply to design for the present, but also to look ahead and attempt to consider if the decisions that are being made will look good in (say) five year's time. Will the fact that the design was implemented in LSI mean that it will appear dated during that time? Will that customised IC or the module that contains it be of use in any other designs? Will the whole technology that you have chosen be around in five year's time? The answers to design problems have to be found in a finite time span, and we can never with safety prophesy what the future will bring; we can, however, predict trends by being aware of current developments and making allowances for them whenever we can.

The total process

All decisions taken by everyone engaged on a project are inter-related. The entire process is dynamic and can be depicted in a diagram such as that in figure 6.2.

The right-hand side of the diagram is the same as figure 6.1, but on the left-hand side a feedback loop has been added to show how decisions must be referred back to the original criteria to judge their effectiveness. The whole design process, whether you are working on your own or as a part of a team, is really a process where information flows through well defined paths.

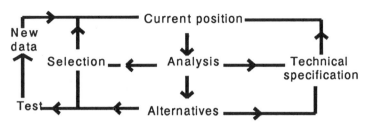

Figure 6.2   The total design process

No matter how confident you may feel about a design it is important to realise the constraints that are present. The list in section 6.3 is not exhaustive but is meant to "flag up" areas which are often overlooked or totally ignored.

6.3 Systems thinking

All systems are made up of smaller sub-systems; every piece of electronic equipment is a carefully chosen selection of components; chosen as a result of careful design. The system's components may be discrete Rs, Cs and transistors, or they may be a collection of VLSI devices. When designing a system think in terms of systems, use manufacturer's literature to find out what is available, and how it can be used directly or with modifications to achieve the systems objectives. Once the technical specification has been decided the system's design begins with a careful analysis of the available sub-systems.

The technical specification in practice

This is the document that will act like a compass to guide you, and a mill-stone to weigh you down when all does not go well. Make sure that you read it and understand it thoroughly.

Try to avoid starting any design work if you do not have a completely clear picture of what it is you are required to design. Avoid at all costs starting work of any kind on a project where the basic ideas are sketched out for you, and the rest of the detail is avoided with a statement like "you-know-what-I-mean". If you do not know what is meant, then say so, then or relatively quickly afterwards; or even if you think you have enough to at least put some thoughts to paper, then when you have written down or drawn "what-it-is-they-mean", ensure that you get their agreement that what you have sketched out is correct. If you accept a project, assuming that you know what is required, but without being absolutely certain, it is you who will be blamed if things go wrong.

The following list is not exhaustive but should give you some ideas of the detail the technical specification should contain.

Inputs and outputs

What are the amplitudes, duration and impedances of the signals that will be input to and output from the circuit? Where do they come from? What are their availability and/or when are they required?

Power and heat

What dc voltages are present? (Or, if you are designing the PSU, what voltages, currents, impedances and regulation will others require?)

What are the constraints on both power that can be consumed and power that can be dissipated? Are there any power supply impedance problems?

Will the packing density of devices on the chosen assembly board either cause problems to, or be caused problems by heat generated by ICs or power dissipating devices?

The requirements for a device which can be plugged into the public electricity supply are vastly different from those which are powered by Ni-Cad batteries or an uninterruptable P.S.U.

The physical environment

What area and hence volume, is available for the circuit?

If you do not know this, you do not know how large your PCB can be and hence how much space is available. This affects the types of devices that can be used, as well as packing densities and heat dissipation.

Is weight a problem?

The requirements for portable, laboratory mobile and fixed installation are vastly different; if the label says "hand-held", there should be no implication that a course in a gymnasium is required as a prerequisite.

What are the constraints on ambient temperature?

A circuit that is going to work as laboratory apparatus will be subject to less temperature stress, than for example, a circuit that is going to operate in a car, here the winter temperature can fall to -25 to -30° C in western Europe, and the summer temperatures can rise (in a car left in full sunlight) to 50-60 °C. Not all ICs are designed for these temperatures, and special devices or ranges (such as the 54xxx series of TTL) may be needed.

What ventilation is planned?

If circuits generate heat (and there are not many that do not), then it will have to be dissipated in some way. Coupled with the previous constraint, this could be an important factor.

This, and the previous discussions on power, should place you in a position to begin to be able to judge whether CMOS (or a CMOS "TTL-look-a-like") is likely to be required to ensure that power and hence heat are not problem.

What factors are to be considered with respect to system reliability?

There is a probability that any electronic component may fail at any time. It is a probability and not a foregone conclusion that this failure is more likely in both the early and latter parts of the life cycle of a system. The well known "bath tub curve" is depicted figure 6.3.

Failures of components are random and cannot be predicted with absolute certainty. However, the likelihood of failure can be predicted, and depending on the degree of reliability required, decisions about the type of components to be used must be taken. The higher the expected reliability of components, the greater the price of the components. An oxide film resistor has an expected failure rate of $0.02 \times 10 E^{-7}/h$ whereas a carbon film resistor has a failure rate of $0.2 \times 10 E^{-6}/h$. The price differential is that the more reliable component is 50% more expensive than the other. When designing for the low-cost, high-volume market, this cost differential may be too great a price to pay. In general, the higher either the working voltage or the power dissipated, then the lower the reliability; variable components such as skeleton and enclosed potentiometers have a far higher assessed failure rate than fixed value components. Manufacturers and sales outlets for all the components to be used in a design can supply figures if this is necessary.

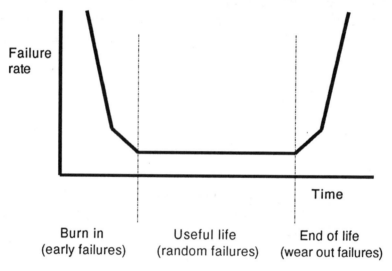

| Burn in | Useful life | End of life |
| (early failures) | (random failures) | (wear out failures) |

Figure 6.3   Failure rate of components and systems

A final word would be that the more components used, the greater the probability of failure, if all other factors are equal; so unless you are going to build-in redundancy or other special features (e.g. majority voting logic), use the minimum number of components that will achieve the required performance.

Are there any special environmental factors?

The design that you are working on may not be part of a space probe, but with the increasing use of electronic systems in all forms of vehicles, the increase in the amount of hand-held and portable equipment may have implications on the design, particularly where the choice of components and method of construction are concerned. Rigidity of PCBs and special-purpose connectors may be necessary if vibration or rapid movement is likely to be a problem.

If operator controls or switches are needed, where can they be placed?

Having placed them, make sure that their position and operating direction will be logical to an operator, in the planned operating environment. Equipment designed for outdoor use must be capable of being operated with gloves on, as well as being waterproof.

What are the ergonomic constraints on the placing of controls?

Which way is a potentiometer to be wired to give a logical increase in an output variable?

Try to think as the operators will, or even better talk to the people who are likely to be the operators and get their views. They, after all, will be using your design and are probably using something similar at the moment; and so can give you good advice.

Where "adjust on test" (aot) or "select on test" (sot) items are required, how can access to these be obtained?

Do not put an aot skeleton potentiometer in a place where someone who lacks articulated fingers or is not a contortionist cannot adjust it and watch the change in an output variable at the same time.

Time and cash constraints

When has your part of the design and the total design to be ready for testing etc.?

The time constraint coupled with the cash constraint are critical, if you are working to a time-table and delivery has been promised on a certain date; then unless exceptional events occur (flood, fire or earthquake are usually accepted as the only valid reasons), you must deliver on that date or take whatever consequences are applicable. Penalty clauses are often inserted into contracts against late delivery. If they are invoked due to your lateness, the results could be dire.

What are the cash constraints?

How much your part of the project costs to produce is vital knowledge, and not a noxious constraint placed on you by "someone in costings". Overrunning a budget is as much bad design as failing to meet any other part of the design criteria.

Test points

What provision is to be made for servicing, repair, maintenance, retrofits and modifications?

Even the best designs fail sometimes and then require repairing. This and tasks such as retrofitting will require measurements to be made on the design, and all this is made far easier if test points are provided. The test points themselves must of course be accessible, and the constraints previously mentioned for the placing of aot and sot items apply here as well. The conditions under which the expected signal should be found will have to be specified by giving the input signals required, as well as the test equipment to be used to conduct the test. Do remember one vital fact, namely that while your laboratory may be equipped with "top-of-the-range" test equipment, test kit in the field may well be different. Unless it is vital that the test is carried out by a "Bloggs and Norton Mk.7/f signal tracer", then do not bother to specify it. Try instead to suggest the type of constraints that apply to the test equipment to be used such as, input impedance, bandwidth and rise and fall times. It is often useful to give two sets of figures, one for the dc levels to be found, and the other for signals that should be present with whatever specified inputs are suggested.

What indicators are to present for the operator?

LEDs do not cost much money and their intelligent inclusion can be a great help in environments where their power consumption is not a factor. Most designs go little further than some device to show that the "ON" switch has been activated, usually by using a red LED. In cases where other LEDs could act as warning of faulty circuit operation, then their inclusion is worthwhile. The temptation when moving from only one LED to including others is that the design may well come to rival Blackpool's famous illuminations if their use is not well thought out. LEDs come now in a variety of colours and in "flashing" and "steady" illuminated states. The change from a steady green light to a flashing red one should alert the operator that all is not well. Where power is at a premium, is it possible to fit an LCD device that can pass on information about system performance?

Specification practicality

Can the specification be realistically met?

Never be afraid to challenge a specification. If you believe that there is something is wrong with it, there may well indeed be something amiss. After a project has been running for a period of time, it is to late to realise that you are reaching for the unattainable. So before you take the responsibility for your part of a project or accept a full project, be sure you know and can achieve the targets.

Design

How flexible is your design?

Two factors emerge here:

(1) If someone else decides that, because of an unforeseen event the technical specification must be altered, and as a result you must change some part of your design, how easy is it to do so? "One-offs" are always needed, but they are expensive enough without having to do a redesign for every minor change that is required. While you are working on the project, remember that some part of it may have to be changed, so at least be aware of the fact.

(2) Every design you work on builds up your own experience. Never try to see any design as simply "a task". Try to view each new challenge as part of your continuing education and training, so that each design should be seen not only as required for its current use but also for possible future use (albeit with modifications) in other circuits.

Test equipment

Do you have, or can you get suitable test equipment?

It is not much use trying to design a digital circuit with a clock rate of 100 MHz if you lack the equipment to inspect waveforms around the circuit. Equipped only with a dc to 20 MHz CRO and an analogue multimeter, you will be unable even to inspect the signal from the clock generator. Work out what you will need and, if it is a non-standard piece of equipment, whether it is obtainable "in-house" or must be hired from an external company. Then ensure you know how long you will want it for. The financial cost of hiring must be set against the cost of the project. The longer you have it, the more it costs; with planning and good design, it is possible to optimise on the use of specialist equipment.

How is the design to be constructed?

A "one-off" design will very probably be made of some form of development or prototyping board, and it is equally likely that wire-ended components will be used. The final product that is produced may well have constraints imposed on it by either BS or MIL specifications, or possibly a device is only available in a wire-ended form when surface mounting components are to be used for the production version. Will a PCB be required as part of the design? If so whose responsibility is that?

Documentation

What form is the documentation to take?

While you are working on the design, you will be recording your work in some form of log book. The way you record your observations could well be altered by the documentation that is needed to support the design. Other people will be using the results of your work, and so to use it effectively they will need to know details of what it is, what it does, how it can be made to do what it does, and perhaps how it does it. At the very least, you will be required to give information on these matters to someone else; you may even have to produce the supporting documentation yourself. Many companies have a "house style" of technical writing which you will have to adhere to; whether they do or do not, there is no excuse for poorly written material. Write in simple, plain English; but you are not producing a work of literary importance, rather a piece of English that will be intelligible to someone who is to use your product.

There are few people who do not wish to switch on a new piece of equipment to "see-what-it-does". If doing so is likely to cause damage unless certain inputs and/or outputs are present, then attach a large warning label to this effect. Make sure that all the information that you give is:

(1) relevant

(2) clear

(3) unambiguous

(4) clarifies rather than confuses

(5) can be understood by the appropriate person.

This last point is worth expanding upon. The person who uses a piece of equipment may well require different information from the person who has installed it or the person who has to service it. This can be illustrated by considering either a television receiver or a small home computer which is used for word processing. In both cases the users may have no technical knowledge at all, and the information they need must reflect this. You will have already seen the products of other people's attempts at technical writing when you have looked at instruction leaflets for domestic appliances; the detail there is vastly different from that given to someone who is going to use a logic analyser. Talking to either a current or potential user of your design is a great help in deciding what your documentation should contain and how it should be written.

Final thoughts

In every case one decision affects others. The whole design model is based on Figure 6.2 and so one passes round the loop every time a decision is taken. A particular decision could affect both the next decision as well as the previous one. Many decisions will involve trade-offs between constraints. There is seldom a "best design" for all the possible features that are to be incorporated, equally there is no route which is 100% sure to produce the optimum design against all constraints. However, following a systematic route such as the one described; could well save time and realise a design that works first time and achieves the technical specification desired.

The Team

It is seldom that you will be working alone on a design. The days are passing where one engineer or technician does the design, development, testing, prototyping, costing, production scheduling and technical writing for a project. In large designs the team may be very large and operating at various sites, even in different countries. The European Airbus and Concord(e) are two obvious examples of this type of project; indeed, the discussions of the constraints of team work on the designs would need a book itself.

Most projects are conducted with a relatively small team of people (3 to 10 is a common figure) and, as it is a team it is expected to work together. It is not expected to work as a group of individuals that calls itself a team but in reality is no such thing. There is a frightening phrase which is almost indefinable: **corporate responsibility.** I take it to mean in effect that each member of the team is jointly responsible for the decisions that are taken and the way the project is run. There will be a team leader, of course, but often one of the leader's chief duties is to guide the team and chase up work that is not forthcoming. The majority of decisions that are taken will be taken by the team itself as a corporate group, so that all individuals are jointly responsible. The "making" of such a group is something that happens during the running of a design; at the start it is often a set of individuals hopefully chosen with the skills to achieve the task.

As a member of that team you need to know what your part of the task is, and who you are responsible to. Assuming you do not want to play the game of being a "meetings man", or always appearing to be the centre of focus by having an important opinion on every topic, then the most important role in team meetings is to listen. It is preferable to listen to what others say and to question more for clarification.

Before every meeting be sure you know why you are going and what you want to know at the end of the meeting that you did not know before it. Write down what it is you want to know do not simply commit it to memory; the human brain is selectively volatile!

What are you going to design ?

This might seem obvious, but unless the team has a technical specification for the design, how on earth is it going to be designed? If you have not been given an outline specification then you will have to draw one up yourself. There are two golden rules:

(1) **Do it in consultation with others.** If you are in a team then you need to consult with fellow team members. They need to know how you are thinking and to be informed of the basis on which you are implementing your work. This does not have to be done formally, but when you have agreed the technical specification, write it down and make sure that the other team members have a copy, not to protect yourself should something unforeseen go wrong, but rather to communicate your joint decisions as an aide mémoire.

(2) **Be prepared to listen.** Other team members will be involved, possibly by supplying inputs to or by taking outputs from your circuit. Other team members could well be affected by your decisions, and have a right to have their views heard and discussed.

These rules do not waste time in any way at all; there is no point being well on the way to finishing your part of the design, only to discover that it will not interface with someone else's part. Such a disaster could well cause the embarrassment of having to start at the beginning again.

An illustrative example (Q.6 p182)

This example is chosen because it is applicable within the domain of digital electronics and requires no specialised external knowledge of control or microprocessor systems. It is adapted from a case study in the Design Council's Engineering Design Teaching Aids Programme.

Q6.1

Figure 6.1.1 shows the seven sections of a seven-segment LCD display. Devise a method of displaying denary numbers on the display.

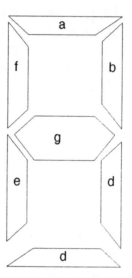

Figure 6.1.1 Seven-segment display

A6.1

Generation of Alternatives.

Alternative 1

Figure 6.1.2 shows the truth table for the display. Segment a is required when 0, 2, 3, 5, 6, 7, 8 and 9 are displayed; while segment b is required when all except 5 and 6 are displayed. Similar arguments would give the requirements for other segments. Hence the combinational logic requirements are:

The Karnaugh maps and their minimised forms are shown in figure 6.1.3.

A similar set of circuit equations could be produced for each of the other segments. It is therefore possible to design logic to decode the

$$a = \overline{A}\,\overline{B}\,\overline{C}\,\overline{D} + \overline{A}\,\overline{B}\,C\,\overline{D} + \overline{A}\,\overline{B}\,C\,D + \overline{A}\,B\,\overline{C}\,D + \overline{A}\,B\,C\,\overline{D} + \overline{A}\,B\,C\,D + A\,\overline{B}\,\overline{C}\,\overline{D} + A\,\overline{B}\,\overline{C}\,D$$

$$b = \overline{A}\,\overline{B}\,\overline{C}\,\overline{D} + \overline{A}\,\overline{B}\,\overline{C}\,D + \overline{A}\,\overline{B}\,C\,\overline{D} + \overline{A}\,\overline{B}\,C\,D + \overline{A}\,B\,\overline{C}\,\overline{D} + \overline{A}\,B\,C\,D + A\,\overline{B}\,\overline{C}\,\overline{D} + A\,\overline{B}\,\overline{C}\,D$$

Binary				Number displayed	Display						
A	B	C	D		a	b	c	d	e	f	g
0	0	0	0	0	1	1	1	1	1	1	0
0	0	0	1	1	0	1	1	0	0	0	0
0	0	1	0	2	1	1	0	1	1	0	1
0	0	1	1	3	1	1	1	1	0	0	1
0	1	0	0	4	0	1	1	0	0	1	1
0	1	0	1	5	1	0	1	1	0	1	1
0	1	1	0	6	1	0	1	1	1	1	1
0	1	1	1	7	1	1	1	0	0	1	0
1	0	0	0	8	1	1	1	1	1	1	1
1	0	0	1	9	1	1	1	1	0	1	1

Figure 6.1.2 Truth table for a seven-segment display

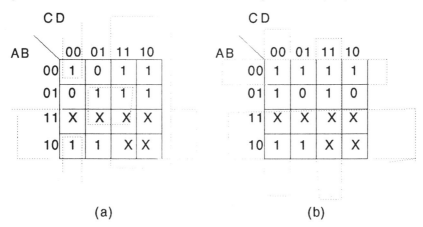

(a)   (b)

Figure 6.1.3 Karnaugh maps for segments a and b

$$a = C + A + BD + \overline{B}\,\overline{D}$$

$$b + A + \overline{AB} + CD + \overline{CD}$$

display. The resultant circuit is quite large in its requirements for both ICs and for space. It could however be implemented as part of a PLA circuit's configuration.

Alternative 2

ICs which are designed to drive LCD displays are available. The selection of these devices is often the most logical one for commercial applications.

Alternative 3

The original article suggested the use of two_74189 RAMs. These would hold the truth table for the display and use the binary values input as A, B, C and D as addresses. The truth table for the two RAMs is shown in figure 6.1.4. and the resultant circuit in figure 6.1.5.

A0	A1	A2	A3	D0	D1	D2	D3		A0	A1	A2	A3	D0	D1	D2	D3
0	0	0	0	1	1	1	1		0	0	0	0	1	1	0	0
0	0	0	1	0	1	1	0		0	0	0	1	0	0	0	0
0	0	1	1	1	1	1	1		0	0	1	0	1	0	1	0
0	0	1	1	1	1	1	1		0	0	1	1	0	0	1	0
0	1	0	0	0	1	1	0		0	1	0	0	0	1	1	0
0	1	0	1	1	0	1	1		0	1	0	1	0	1	1	0
0	1	1	0	1	0	1	1		0	1	1	0	1	1	1	0
0	1	1	1	1	1	1	0		0	1	1	1	0	1	0	0
1	0	0	0	1	1	1	1		1	0	0	0	1	1	1	0
1	0	0	1	1	1	1	1		1	0	0	1	0	1	1	0

Truth table for RAM 1   Truth table for RAM 2

Figure 6.1.4 Truth tables for storing a look up table for seven-segment decoding

Evaluation of alternatives

Alternative 1 would require a large number of ICs; it would take up a lot of space and would need a PCB to be designed for it. Except for the satisfaction of producing and testing the resultant circuit, there is little to recommend it.

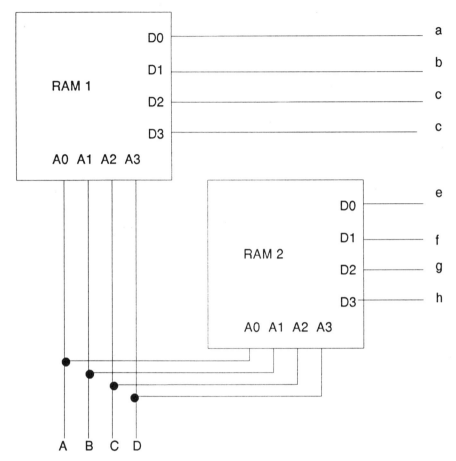

Figure 6.1.5 Two RAMs configured to drive a seven-segment display

Alternative 2 is a stock item. It would probably be the easiest and cheapest to implement.

Alternative 3 has the advantage that the displayed pattern could be altered at will, for example the table in the RAM could display alphabet characters as well as numerical ones. If a RAM were not feasible the circuit could be implemented using a ROM, in which case, however, the flexibility of changing the display would not be present. The solution using RAM would of course require the RAMs to have some means of being loaded with the truth table stored in them.

For the fastest solution, the use of readily available ICs is the best; other constraints may, however, make one of the other solutions preferable. In this example and in many other design problems there is often no "best" solution; a compromise between conflicting constraints may be needed.

Appendix 1

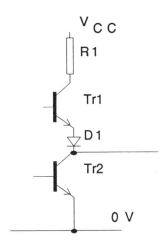

Figure 1.1 NAND gate "totem-pole" output circuit

Figure 1.1 shows the normal output circuit for a TTL NAND gate. Tr1 and Tr2 are known as a "totem pole" circuit, they form a low impedance output circuit for both the HIGH and the LOW output states. However, this means that the outputs of gates cannot be wired together, such a connection would cause the output transistors to overheat when one of the gates was HIGH and another LOW. When Tr4 and the diode D1 are switched off by the input at the base of Tr1, there is no connection between the output and V_{CC}. The diode ensures that Tr1 is OFF while TR2 is ON. This occurs during the output of a LOW state from the gate, Tr2 will act as a current sink for the maximum number of 10 TTL inputs that can be connected to the output.

When conditions are reversed to output a HIGH, then Tr1 is ON and T2 is OFF, in this state a Logic 1 is output via Tr1 and D1.

187

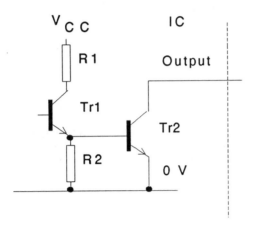

Figure 1.2 Open collector output circuit

Figure 1.2 shows the output circuit of a 7401, which is an open collector NAND device. There is no collector load resistor fitted internally on the IC. This connection is made externally, when they are wired in this way they can form a "wired-OR" or a "wired-AND" configuration. The way an open collector device can be connected to form a wired AND gate is shown in figure 1.3.

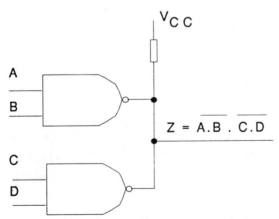

$$Z = \overline{A.B} . \overline{C.D}$$

Figure 1.3 A "wired-AND" configuration from 7401 oc gates

Appendix 2

The outline for J and N packaging for TTL gates are shown in figures 2.1. and 2.2.

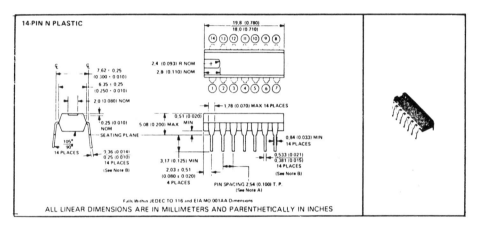

Figure 2.1 14-pin N plastic packaging

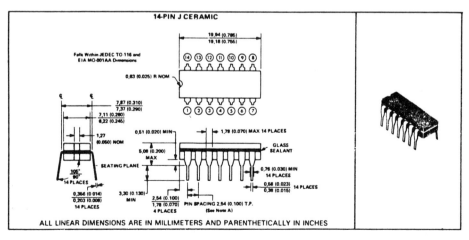

Figure 2.2 14-pin J ceramic packaging

189